PEEPING DOWN
THE BOMB SIGHT

PEEPING DOWN THE BOMB SIGHT

Carl L. Crocker

TEMPLE PUBLISHING COMPANY
London, England

First published in Great Britain 1995
by Temple Publishing Company
Edinburgh House,
19 Nassau Street,
London W1N 7RE

**British Library Cataloguing-in-Publication Data.
A catalogue record for this book is available
from the British Library**

ISBN 1 85977 065 7

Cover design by Harold King

The characters and situations in this book
are entirely imaginary and bear no relation
to any real person or actual happening.

Printed & bound in England by
Antony Rowe Ltd, Chippenham, Wiltshire

This book is Dedicated
to my adopted son Seyhan

Acknowledgement

The author wishes to acknowledge the many
Turkish friends who became a part of his life
during his many years in Turkey.

Chapter One

It was a brilliant warm summer afternoon in 1956 as I sat gazing out of my office window in the Flight Determination Laboratory at White Sands Proving Grounds, New Mexico. I was just having a breather after getting off of the telephone with the Officer-In-Charge of the Range Mission at Holloman Air Force Base also located in New Mexico, just 25 miles from White Sands Proving Grounds. Something happened which shouldn't have happened. One of our Nike Missiles blew the piss out of their practice aircraft drones which shouldn't have happened. Boy, it sure blew it right out of the sky clean and sweet. However, that isn't what was supposed to happen. What should have happened was the Nike Missile was supposed to have come close to the drone and simulate blowing the drone up. It would appear that someone in the Field Measurement Branch of the Flight Determination Laboratory must have gone to sleep and was a bit late in pushing the button. The next thing we knew the drone had taken a direct hit and then all hell broke loose. I really don't know why the Major was so damn angry as we only had done it the previous week after we told him that we would be very careful on future missions. I tried to defuse the situation a wee bit and add a little humour to our conversation. I told him that we were very careful but his drone zigged when it should have zagged and hit our missile. Further, we should be the ones complaining as his drone knocked our missile out of the sky. With that statement I held the telephone as far away from me as I could. By his language I can surely tell you he didn't buy one word of it. Frankly, I could safely say he was really pissed off with what was pouring forth from the telephone. I finally put the telephone down and let him rave on while I did something else. When he finished, I said, 'thank you' and hung up the telephone. I figured a person could get all bent up listening to that crap day in and day out so I just put the phone down and let them get it out of their system. Systems! that reminds me that I have to get my daily input into the Remington Rand (Brain) Computer or they will be blowing me out of my chair.

Marci has just entered my office with the afternoon distribution. Marci is Colonel Rombley's secretary and has been for sometime. She is a very stunning looking lady about 36 or 37 years of age, about 5 feet 7 inches tall with an olive complexion, dark hair and dark flashing eyes. 'Carl, Colonel Rombley would like to see you in his office at your convenience.'

'Thank you Marci. By the way Marci, did Colonel Rombley relate the subject matter to you?'

'No Carl, but I can say he received a letter from General Hall and he wasn't very happy about it.'

'Thanks again Marci.'

'Good afternoon Colonel,' I said with a spark in my voice.

'Come in Carl,' as he motioned with his hand. He was on the telephone to someone. 'Please have a seat.' He had never called me by my first name and I was taken aback by it. He completed his telephone conversation, placed the telephone down, then turned to me. 'Carl' he started, 'I have just received a letter from General Hall that has displeased me very much. He is requesting me to relieve you from your assignment here in the Flight Determination Laboratory and reassigning you to the Integrated Range Mission in his headquarters.'

'Did General Hall give you any reason for his request other than the fact that he is a General of this installation and his word is law?'

'After reading his letter, I requested a meeting with him and he responded very quickly. At our meeting, I told him that you were a very important and intricate part of my operation and I would find it nearly impossible to find another person of your calibre to fit into your position.'

'What did he have to say about that?'

'Oh he agreed fully, but stated his priority was far more pressing than that of the Flight Determination Laboratory. Do you recall Carl the big vehicle project you accomplished for the Integrated Range Mission a few months ago when the Fourth United States Army, at Fort Sam Houston, wanted to take 14 vehicles away from White Sands Proving Grounds because they claimed that they were not being utilised?'

2

'Colonel, how in the hell could I ever forget that back-breaking project. By the way, did you ever hear what the final outcome was due to my study and report?'

'Yes, General Hall let me read the final results. Due to your studies, charts and maps of the area of concern, the Commanding General of the Fourth United States Army made a complete determination based on your studies and report decided that we could not only retain our 14 vehicles but granted White Sands Proving Grounds an additional 16 new vehicles. General Hall's feelings are, if you can outgun the Commanding General of the Fourth US Army, your attributes and brain power are not fully utilised to their fullest in your current assignment. Therefore, he wants you assigned to the Integrated Range Mission along with such people as Weiner Von Braun and Clyde Tombaugh to name just a few.'

'Colonel Rombley, just what in hell do I have in common with Dr Weiner Von Braun, renowned scientist and Dr Clyde Tombaugh also a renowned astronomer?'

'Nothing that I can see.'

'To tell the truth Colonel Rombley, I'm really happy in my assignment in the Flight Determination Laboratory and desire to remain here.'

'Carl, I know just how you feel, believe me I do, but after all, General Hall wears the star and I the eagle. Further, he is the Commanding General of this installation, end of conversation.'

Three days later I was transferred to the Integrated Range Mission and given a very highly polished and impressive looking desk. Just for good measure, they threw in a huge walk-in-room safe containing and controlling all Classified Documents and material coming into this installation. I was told that I was given this job in the interim as the person I was to replace had not left that position or the headquarters.

Fighting this paper war day after day was really not my cup of tea or coffee or what have you. Every document that comes into this headquarters plus leaving has to be receipted for. Back in the early days of old San Francisco the same principle applied so far as it pertained to the Chinese laundry. That is, no ticki no laundry. In this case, no receipt, no document. In other words, whoever saw the document or had it pass through their hands had to sign for that document. I was processing between 25 and 35 Top Secret Documents each day and on top of that I had to make personal deliveries of some of these documents when they were marked 'For Your Eyes Only'. In that case, the person's name would be stated. If possible, you delivered that document to the person concerned. However, there were times when that wasn't possible so you notified the person concerned. Anytime that I had to leave my office regardless of the reason, I had to lock my walk-in safe, sign the document on the door of the safe stating the time of locking and verified by another person and also stating the date. Oh yes, just one little mistake, like leaving the safe open while you dashed off to the little boy's room with your touch of diarrhoea or placing yourself in a position where you cannot see your safe clearly at all times, could lead you to the Lazy Daisy Rest Home at Fort Levenworth, Kansas, for a number of years behind bars. Thank you, I just don't care for some.

As the days and weeks dragged on, I'm no nearer to my assignment I was sent to the Integrated Range of Mission to fill. I told myself I would give them another month before I went to see General Hall and ask him to send me back to the Flight Determination Laboratory (FDL). This classified business I was in charge of was exciting in some ways, but mostly it was becoming a drag. I would say that 99% of the people I dealt with were just great, but the 1% were in my opinion were just ratbags. Case in point involved one of the scientists I shall call Dr Thomas. Needless to say, he was one of the better paid scientists at the Sands with whom people just didn't mess with. Early on a Tuesday afternoon after lunch, I received a 'Red Hot' Top Secret Document from Huntsville, Alabama, which I had been informed that the good Dr Thomas was urgently expecting. After my initial processing of the document, I closed my walk-in safe and went directly to Dr Thomas' office. When I arrived at his office, I found that his secretary was not in her office. I noticed that Dr Thomas' door was slightly opened so I quietly knocked on the door thinking that he could be giving his secretary some dictation. As I opened the door there was Dr Thomas sitting in his chair at his desk and really snoring up a storm. I quietly left his office and started back to my office. I surely wasn't the one who was going to wake him up from his afternoon snooze. Just as I was closing the door to the secretary's office she was just returning.

'What are you doing here she blurted at me?'

'I have a Top Secret Document which is for Dr Thomas 'eyes only'.'

'I'll take it,' she demanded.

'Sorry Joyce, but this is marked for Dr Thomas eyes only and you are not Dr Thomas. When the good Dr is not too busy, call me and I'll bring the document back.' With that statement, she gave me one hell of a dirty look. I smiled and said, 'Sorry, Joyce, that's the rules and in this case I call the shots.' At no time did I say I caught the good Dr Thomas sleeping in his office to anyone. As far as I was concerned that was his business and none of mine. I returned to my office and opened the safe and started to process more classified documents. By this time, the afternoon mail had arrived. In approximately twenty-five minutes I see the good Dr Thomas hustle his bustle into Captain Joy's office. Shortly, Captain Joy, who is my boss at the office, gets up from his desk and closes the door that leads to my office. That's not so unusual, as often times they do hold private conversations. Shortly, Captain Joy opened the door and requested me to come into his office. I locked the safe and entered Captain Joy's office. 'Yes Sir, may I help you?'

'Sergeant Crocker, Dr Thomas has brought two serious complaints against you. One was for interrupting his important thought on a very important military subject. The second was for being discourteous to Dr Thomas's secretary. You know Sergeant Crocker that shows a disgraceful lack of military discipline on your part and gives the Military Service a very black eye. I'm having a notation made of this and having it placed in your 201 File. That's all I want to say. You are dismissed.'

'Captain Joy.'

'I said you are dismissed Sergeant.'

'Yes Sir.' I stood there and just looked at the Captain in utter disbelief as to what he had just related to me. I wasn't given a chance to say anything or even defend myself one way or the other. I was guilty and case closed. Had I been allowed to speak I could have told the 'good' Captain that Dr Thomas was sound asleep and snoring up a storm and his secretary wanted me to give her a Top Secret Document which was marked for Dr Thomas' 'eyes only'. In short, Dr Thomas was playing CYA (Cover Your Ass). The good Dr must have thought that I had gone back and told everyone that he was asleep in his office etc. However, even Dr Thomas and Captain Joy didn't know that the document I was taking to Dr Thomas was marked for Dr Thomas' 'eyes only'. This is the part that the good secretary had left out of her story when telling the Dr. When I came out of the Captain's office, Warrant Officer Walker could see that something was radically wrong. He asked me and I told him. He said that he was going to have a word with Captain Joy and I told him to just forget it. I checked to insure that my walk-in safe was locked and told Warrant Officer Walker I would be back in a short while. Knowing I was very upset, he didn't ask where I was going and let the subject drop. I didn't know at the time, but what I was about to do would change my entire life from that day to the present day.

As I entered the Personnel Office I was greeted by Chief Warrant Officer Kolwalski while he was on the telephone. He motioned for me to have a chair and that he would be right with me in a minute or two. I nodded okay.

Okay now, he said and wanted to know what was on my mind.

'It's like this Sir. I was just wondering what, if anything, you had in the way of an overseas assignment?'

'Funny you should ask that question, as I've just today received a request in from the Adjutant General's Office in Washington DC looking for an Administrative Sergeant in the field of MOS 717.6 or 717.7 (Military Occupation Specialist) for an assignment to the Military Mission in Turkey.'

'My God, I wonder if that would be like an assignment to the French Foreign Legion?'

'I have no idea Sergeant Crocker. Take all the time you want, just so I have an answer by 0900 hours tomorrow.'

'Turkey . . . huh? At this point in time I'm so damnably angry at Captain Joy and his actions that I believe leaving the Integrated Range Mission would best serve my Military Career and get me out of a very poor situation. Okay Sir, submit my name as a possible person for that position in Turkey.'

I return to my office after having been gone for about thirty minutes. As I enter my office, I see that Joyce, Dr Thomas' secretary is standing by my desk all puffed up like a strutting peacock. As she looked at me she was saying in her mind, Well Mister, I've sure put you in your place today and don't forget it. I opened my walk-in safe and sat down at my desk. Take care of the lady one, Colonel said. I started to say, she is no lady, but thought better of it.

'May I help you Joyce?'

'Yes,' came a nasty snarling remark. 'I've come to get Dr Thomas' Classified Document which you didn't give me this afternoon, what else?'

'In that case, would you please inform the good Dr Thomas that since this documents is marked for "his eyes only" that he will have to come and sign for it. Under no circumstances will I give it to you.

Thank you,' I said. With that remark from me, she got very angry, stomped her foot, broke wind and literally flew out of my office with a very nasty foul smell trailing behind her. With a sudden roar, I thought the two Colonels were going to lose control of their bladders as they just doubled up laughing. I don't know which one of the Colonels it was that opened the window, but thank God he did before we were all overcome with the foul smell. While still laughing, the other Colonel said, 'She must have had Mexican chilli and onions for lunch to create such a blast.'

I finally said, 'I'm very sorry for the side show gentlemen, how may I help you?'

'You are Sergeant Crocker?'

'Yes Sir.'

'This is Colonel Shelton and I'm Colonel Hoffman.'

'Pleased to meet you gentlemen. How may I help you?'

'Sergeant, we are on our installation check to see just how classified material is controlled at your installation and other installations in the Fourth United States Army area. We work out of the Inspector General's office and report back to them. However, from what we have witnessed here just a few minutes ago, we feel more than certain that you are strictly following the official rules relating to classified material and its proper handling. This will be in our report back to the Inspector General Office at Fort Sam Houston, Texas. However, we do have one important suggestion to make.'

'What is that Sir?'

'That is, that you make available extra gas masks just in case of another gas attack.'

For the next two weeks I performed my duties in the Integrated Range Mission like nothing had ever happened. My First Sergeant and my Commanding Officer knew that I had put in for an overseas assignment and they assumed that I had informed Captain Joy of my pending assignment. Nothing could have been further from the truth as I didn't tell a soul in the Integrated Range Mission headquarters. It wasn't that I was forgetful, or being mean, but rather being just plain nasty. Since I had gotten my ass chewed out for trying to do the right thing, I decided not to tell Captain Joy and let him chew me out again. Either way, I was in a no win situation, so to hell with it.

Prior to closing my office my very good friend Sergeant Herb Zig, who is General Hall's driver, stopped by to see if I'm getting ready to leave. He seldom has time to stop and talk as the General is not far behind. From where I sit, I can see him dash out, uncover the one star from the front and back bumper, run around and open the door for the General, close the door and leap into the front seat. To me it seems a little funny as Herb is 6 feet 3 inches tall and weighing about 220 pounds and dashing around the car and then leaping behind the wheel with a graceful leap. However, I feel quite certain that members of the Russian Bolshoi Ballet are in no jeopardy of being done out of a job by Herb. The only thing I got out of Herb's conversation, if you could call it a conversation was that he would meet me in the Consolidated Mess Hall after he had disposed of the General. That sounds a little ominous, but I understand what he meant.

Friday night and I should have known that it would be stinking fish for the evening meal. I dislike fish in any fashion shape or form. It's a long story, but as a young child growing up my father had his boat and would go deep sea fishing. Bringing his bountiful catch home, it was my job to gut the fish and cut off their heads, not to mention scaling same. However, the worse part was, that if I didn't eat all of my fish for my evening meal, father saw to it that I had it for breakfast the following morning. If I still didn't finish it for breakfast, I had it for lunch. Now ask me why I dislike fish. Over here Herb.

'Hi buddy. Carl, what is the matter and why the rather serious look?'

'I guess I should tell you. Herb, how long have we been good friends?'

'I'd say about two and a half years.'

'Yep, that's about right. Herb, I'm leaving White Sands Proving Grounds and heading overseas.'

'You're joking.'

'No Herb, Chief Warrant Officer Kolwalski called me today and told me that the Department of the Army has sent him the funding allocation and the authority to cut my orders.'

'Where in hell do you think you are going?'

'I'm being assigned to a mission headquarters in Turkey with further assignment to a place called Erzurum, Turkey.'

'Erzurum, Turkey,' Herb repeats.

'Well, you know what that is Carl,' trying to make a joke. 'It's a place where naughty Sergeants go for upsetting Dr Thomas.'

'Herb, that's not even remotely funny.'

'You're right Carl, but you must admit it sounds different. Anyway, it sounds pretty far out.'

'Far out, it's located very near the Russian border.'

'The hell you say. You have told your boss Captain Joy you are leaving haven't you?'

'Hell no.'

'What in hell is that little shit ass going to do when you tell him?'

'I haven't the foggiest idea and above all I couldn't care less.'

'I'll tell you Carl what is going to happen. He'll crap in his uniform pants, then run crying to General Hall and try to stop you from leaving.'

'It will be much too late Herb, as these orders are coming from Washington, DC and there isn't a damn thing either one of them can do about it. The part that is going to kill Captain Joy is that he is going to have to take a complete physical inventory of all the classified documents, of which there hundreds, and prove that they are all there and have correct covering receipts for all documents.'

'That's going to be one hell-of-a-job Carl.'

'Herb, tell me about it.'

'Have you informed General Hall that you are leaving?'

'No.'

'You know Carl, both General Hall and Mrs Hall think the world of you for all your help at this installation and the activities you have fully supported.'

'Be that as it may Herb, there comes a time when you have to take control of your life and make hard strong decisions.'

'Turkey you say Carl. Isn't that the place where they have apartments for females in a Mohammedan household?'

'Herb, I don't know.'

'Yep, they are all dancing girls, beautiful dancing girls and when the Sultan claps his hands the girls all jump up and start dancing.'

'Herb, just where in hell do you get all your good information?'

'From the movies, of course.'

'Has anyone ever told you lately that you are full of crap? The movies. This is 1956, and they have a President and a Prime Minister, no Sultans. Let's get out of this fire trap, as the smell of fish is about to get me down. What have you planned for this evening Herb?'

'I'll watch a little TV and go and hit the sack. What about you?'

'I have some studying to do so the choir will have something to fall back on when I depart. See you tomorrow.'

Another beautiful morning with the morning sun spraying its beautiful metallic rays all over the Oregon Mountains from top to bottom. After spending three years in the lush greenery of Honshu, Japan and then being dropped into the desert of south-western United States sure was a change which was hard adjusting to. As time passes, you learn to adjust and accept your surroundings and appreciate God's handiwork.

Sitting here looking out of the window, I'm having a little case of the backward looks at the present time. Just what have I done with my time here at White Sands Proving Grounds! When I arrived here I was appointed a Platoon Sergeant, a position I'm still holding and will until the day I leave. By an odd stroke of luck I was appointed Choir Director of the Post Chapel Choir, just because there wasn't anyone else that could who would take the position. There wasn't any monetary remuneration attached to the position, but only hard work. The rest of my time I managed to keep myself busy by being appointed Chairman of the Post Army Emergency Relief Fund, Chairman of the March of Dimes Drive, Director of the Post Bridge Club, finally being elected to the Board of Directors of the Non-Commission Officers' Club. The latter position bent the Post Chaplain's nose out of shape and he took offence to it. I finally told him that he could either accept my current situation as it was, or else find himself another Choir Director. That may have not been the Christian thing to do, but I'm getting tired of people imposing themselves on me for their own gain. I told the Chaplain that I wasn't there boozing it up, but only conducting military official business. It only points to the fact that some people are very narrow minded and couldn't care less about you only to feed their own ego.

As I was discussing with Herb just a few weeks ago concerning that which is called the Desert Road. This road leads from White Sands Proving Ground all the way to El Paso, Texas. There have been a number of stories related by the Military Police by having their Guard House at the point where the Desert Road and the Post meet. In short, the Guard House is stuck out in the middle of nowhere and I mean nowhere. I've heard some rather strange stories about how rattlesnakes and tarantulas come right into the Guard House and wanting to keep the Military Police company on cold winter nights. Between thee and me, I know who would have the Guard House and it wouldn't be me.

'Herb, you know the story, just what would you do?'

'Me! I'd kick his or her ass up between their forked tongues and let them merrily freeze to death.'

'That sounds good, but what about the tarantulas.'

'Just one step and they're gone.'

'Yuk!'

'I hear you whistling Dixie Herb. Speaking about that, just last week, Herb, one of the men from the Doppler Section was dropped off to open his station and nearly had a heart attack when he opened the door. Sitting there pretty as you please were two six-foot rattlesnakes waiting to greet him upon his arrival. The funny part is that they must have slipped in the day before when he was manning the station and he didn't see them. The poor kid had to report to the Range Mission as to why he was late in getting his station on air.'

Further, during that time he brought up a rather strange topic by asking whatever happened to that girl I used to have working for me when I was assigned to the Field Measurement Branch.

'What was her name?' he asked.

'Which one?'

'You know the one I mean, the very plain Jane.'

'Oh you are referring to Betty.'

'That's the one.'

'Well Herb, when she came to work in my office I just couldn't believe that Civilian Personnel would hire someone like Betty. She was about as plain as you could get with no personality showing anywhere. Her hair was blackish brown, straight, wore no make up, bushy eyebrows not shaped, and the dress she wore was a washable house dress. Further, she wore no socks only sandals. They said that she had the required qualifications, so they hired her. She was always clean, but that is about all you could say for her. However, about six months later when that airman came into my office on business, she stopped him and she spoke to him for about thirty minutes. I was a little uptight as there was plenty of work to be gotten out. As I recall, she stayed back that night and completed all the required work. It must have been about two weeks later when she told me that she thought that she was in love with Peter, the airman from Holloman Air Force Base. All I could see in her eyes was cloud nine. Another week went by when she came into work and all I could do was just stand there and gook at her. I didn't stare at her, I gooked. Finally I said to this person standing there, is that you Betty?'

'Yes Sergeant Crocker, whom were you expecting, Elizabeth Taylor?' Even with her brilliant response, all I could do was look at her. She was dressed in a beautiful royal blue knit one piece dress which really showed off her hour-glass figure, and the sand had not settled at the bottom either. She wore a very nice gold pin over her left breast with matching ear rings and a thin gold belt. Her footwear consisted of black silk stockings with black high heel patent leather shoes. Now if that wasn't enough, she had her hair done in sort of a soft upsweep at the sides and dyed black to get rid of the brown streaks, finishing it off with a hair cut and a soft perm. To further add to the transformation, she had her black eye brows shaped and wore light blue eyeshadow. When she came in to get my distribution I finally had drummed up enough courage to say, shake it Betty, but don't break it. Herb, she walked out of my office with her back still towards me, stopped, turned her head, looked over her right shoulder, smiled and said, 'Sergeant Crocker, it's all ass not glass,' and left my office. Needless to say, I had been beautifully put in my place, but nicely. As best as I can remember, Betty lasted about two weeks longer, and she and Peter, the airman from Holloman Air Force Base, went off and got married. Never heard from her again.'

'Now that you are leaving Carl, I suppose you do have some fond memories of this place don't you?'

'Sure Herb, there are a lot of very fond memories, some more fonder than others. This one as an example occurred during one of my choir rehearsals. As usual, it was one of those Thursday nights when I had one hell of a day at the office and I wanted the rehearsal to go as smoothly as possible so I could accomplish getting two new anthems in the mill so to speak, for the coming weeks. As luck would have it, when I was working with the tenors and basses, the women sat there and gossiped to the point that I could no longer hear the men's parts and had to stop. I told them, 'Ladies, please study your parts, as I will be coming to you next.' I turned and started with the men again. Shortly, the ladies were at it full bore once again. I stopped once again and said, 'Mrs Kershaw, would you please stand up and tell all of us the subject of your conversation? I'm sure that all of us would be most delighted to hear your words of wisdom.' Slowly, she gets up while still laughing. 'What we are talking about was the Post Cake Baking Contest this coming Sunday and I was trying to find out just how many had entered.

You are holding up the choir rehearsal to find out about the Post

Cake Baking Contest? There must be a connection somewhere, but I fail to see it. Further ladies, if I couldn't bake a cake better than all of you I wouldn't even be talking about it. Now shall we all get back down to some good honest choir work? Now if that isn't possible, just remember the door swings both ways and don't let it hit you in the backside on your way out. Herb, what are you laughing about?'

'You told the ladies and the people in the choir not to let the door hit them in the backside on the way out?'

'I could have been rude and told them not to let the door hit them in the ass on the way out, but I was polite.'

'Then what happened?'

'From that point forward we had an excellent rehearsal. Come Sunday morning, the ladies and things in general all seemed too nice which led me to believe that something was up and rotten in Denmark. It wasn't too long before my beliefs were well and truly confirmed. Mrs Kershaw and several other ladies of the choir came up to me and told me that they had entered my name into the Post Cake Baking Contest which was being held at the Enlisted Men's Service Club at 1500 hours. Laughing and seemingly to get her jollies off she even went one step further by saying that her kitchen was completely at my disposal. It had become obvious that the hour of truth had arrived and the monkey was placed squarely on my back. Now, it was time for me to either put up or shut up. After church, I asked, 'Could we stop by my barracks to get a few items?' 'Sure, no problem.' I went upstairs and picked up a few little items, placed them in a plastic bag and away we went. Arriving at the Kershaws' residence I was shown to the kitchen and with her blessing was told to have a good time. She closed the door and went off laughing. While showing me the kitchen, she also revealed where the alcohol spirits were hiding unbeknowning to her. I made a mental note just in case and filed it away should I require it later. What kind of cake was I going to make from scratch (a requirement) so I wouldn't become the laughing stock. I stuck my neck out and there were a few people ready to chop it off with no remorse. I remember as a younger man in San Diego my family always liked my one egg cake as it didn't cost too much to make and it tasted pretty good. When I got to the stage that I needed to add the vanilla flavouring I found that it was nearly empty. Oh shit, what am I going to do now? I sat down at the table to ponder my current crisis. The mental note I had made earlier suddenly occurred to me. That's it. I'll use the rum I saw in the kitchen and follow it through to the frosting. During this time, no one was allowed to enter the kitchen as it was my private domain until I came out. Brother, did that cake ever smell real good and just reeking of rum. The two round pans were rising just beautifully with a golden crust on top. Since I had reduced the heat to 350 degrees instead of the 375, the cakes took longer to bake but raised evenly. Now they were ready to take out of the oven to cool. While I had the rum frosting all made up, I was thinking of something rather special and different so far as the decorations were concerned. With the frosting, I took my little space craft and rubbed the rum frosting all over it. Next I took a ping-pong ball, coloured it blue with food colouring and placed it on top of the cake. With a wire attached to the space craft and sunk into the cake, I coloured the wire with yellow food colouring to give the impression of a vapour trail as the space craft sped into space. It wasn't half bad even if I say so myself. However, there was something special about that cake which set it aside from the rest. It reeked of strong rum. When all was ready, we drove down to the Enlisted Men's Club and my cake was placed in the judging area. Even from five feet away you could still smell the rum. It was now up to the judges to make the final judgment. As I looked around, most of the choir ladies were on hand as most of them had made cakes and entered them in the contest. When your cake is entered in the contest, you are given a number so the judges don't know which cake belongs to whom. There were five tables with cakes on them and one table with no cake on it. We didn't have too long to wait as the judges came in and walked around the tables. They made a selection of about a dozen cakes and they were placed on the empty table. They walked around again and selected about three more cakes. After a few more walk abouts they stopped at this one cake which was in the shape of WSPG Headquarters Building. It was made by a military professional baker. It took 1st Place. Now who was going to fill the next two places. General Hall was one of the judges and he walked around the table being judged several times then stopped at my cake. He reached down and put his finger on the frosting, tasted it and said Number 39 has taken 2nd Place. How did I know he liked rum. I let out a yell and my choir members just looked at me. When it was all over, not one of my choir members even got a mention. I just looked at them, not saying a word, but really saying, 'I told you so.' The cakes were auctioned off to the highest bidder the money going to the March of Dimes. Funny, the subject never came up again.

14

Other fond memories I have had of WSPG occurred in the chapel. I would always tell the Chaplain's Assistant to wait at the back of the chapel until the choir had finished singing *Praise God From Whom All Blessings Flow* before he went down the aisle. Nothing seemed to work so I told him that one day I would drop a book on his head since the choir was in the balcony. It became obvious that nothing was going to change him. So . . . . this particular Sunday I had made up my mind as to my course of action prior to the collection being taken. On top of all that, I had warned him that very Sunday morning to be very careful. He had just received the first collection plate from the left side of the chapel and was waiting for the second plate to be received from the right side of the chapel. Just as he was about to take his first step towards the altar. I pushed my hymnal over the balcony. The surprise was so great and shocking that he dropped the collection plate and the sound of money going in all directions sure broke the tranquillity of the morning service. He looked up at me while I looked down at him. Two of the ushers helped him retrieve the money while we finished singing, *Praise God From Whom All Blessings Flow.*'

'What happened next Carl?'

'Nothing, as we never had a repeat performance.'

Chapter Two

So far this working week, I have managed to get by without telling the ever loving Captain Joy that I'm leaving on Friday. I'll have to tell him tomorrow, as it will give him Wednesday and Thursday to get the classified inventory taken. He is sure going to get his knickers in a knot when he is confronted with this little problem.

Armed with the clearance papers, I knocked on Captain Joy's door and waited for him to say enter. With a grunt, which is sort of a guttural sound, he bids me enter. 'What's on your mind Sergeant?'

'Sir, I've just come in to let you know that I'm leaving your establishment and White Sands.'

'As you can see Sergeant, I'm very busy this morning so please state your business and make it short.' With that sort of remark, I said, 'Thank you Sir,' saluted, turned around and left his office. He didn't have a clue as to what I had said to him and I sure in hell could have cared less. If I wanted to be catty, I could tell you that he didn't even return my salute, but I won't. Once a dick head, always a dick head, but once again I wouldn't say that.

I returned to my office and related to Warrant Officer Walker what had transpired in Captain Joy's office. I suggested that the Captain had better get 'hot' with the classified inventory as I was leaving on Friday. Later that morning Warrant Officer Walker went into Captain Joy's office and told him that I was leaving on Friday.

'Why didn't Sergeant Crocker come in and tell me himself?'

'He did this morning, but you obviously didn't pay any attention to him so he left.'

'Now you tell me I have to complete the classified inventory prior to his leaving on Friday?'

'That's right Captain.'

'I'll go and see General Hall concerning this situation as I'm much too busy for such things. I'll have General Hall cancel these orders as I'm much too busy with other things.'

'Captain Joy, with all due respects Sir, these orders were issued from Washington, DC and have nothing to do with General Hall.

With much bellyaching, biting of nails, cursing, and raising hell in general, Captain Joy plus working two days and nights finally completed the inventory. All documents were accounted for and he signed for them. Now all he had to do was to sign my clearance papers and all was complete. When I entered his office for the signing of my papers, he looked at me like I was a little green man from outer space. Further, I learned a long time ago that when people bellow and shout loudly, it is only to hide their own inadequacies which they are trying to cover up. In Captain Joy's case, it was the lack of his administrative attributes which he was trying to hide. Be that as it may, he just looked at me and signed my clearance papers. I knew, he knew, we both knew, that he didn't possess enough fortitude to say thank you for a job well done. Knowing that, I just said, 'thank you' and let it go at that.

With all that drama behind me, I didn't go to the office on Friday morning as I had my packing to get accomplished and send my baggage on to McGuire Air Force Base, in New Jersey. When I had that accomplished I went round saying goodbye to many of my friends and to General Hall. When I went to Colonel Rombley's office to say goodbye, Marci had a nice flat cake made with a dancing girl on top. In a way, it was sad leaving as I had accomplished so much and now I was tossing it all in, so to speak.

Herb drove me to the El Paso Airport where I caught my Continental Airline flight to San Diego, California. It was most difficult saying goodbye to Herb as he had been one of my best friends while I was at White Sands Proving Grounds.

The flight seemed like it had just taken off when it was time to fasten seat belts as we were landing in San Diego. Once on the ground, I headed for the baggage area and sure enough Uncle Harry was right there to greet me. He got the luggage and walked to the car. From the airport to my home is only about seven to ten minutes. Mum was there and greeted me at the door with a big hug and plenty of kisses. From there we headed into the dining room where a big steak was about ready to greet me as well.

For the next two weeks Mum Hazel and I went to see many places did so many things, above all seeing so many of her old friends that she hadn't seen in such a long time. We had been on the go from morning till night, but the main thing was she was most happy. When it became time for me to head back to the military and McGuire Air Force Base, Mum said that she would bake a lot of chocolate chip cookies and send them on to me so I would have them for Christmas.

The day before Thanksgiving we completed our processing and would depart McGuire Air Force Base the day after Thanksgiving. I called home and Mum Hazel said that things in general were just great and that she would be having Thanksgiving Dinner with Rose Webber and her family. That eased my mind as I knew that she would not be on her own on Thanksgiving.

The following morning I was up early as we had to have our duffel bag ready to be picked up and taken to the C-54 Cargo Section of the plane. When that was accomplished, we just waited to be taken to the plane and be loaded. The plane was located at the far end of the runway ready to warm up its engines and take off. While we were sitting there a jeep came alongside the C-54. Shortly over the intercom a voice said, Sergeant Crocker, will you please come forward. I thought to myself, now what in the hell is wrong. I have my passport and my shots have all been completed, could by chance, I've gotten on the wrong aircraft? When I had gotten to the front of the aircraft, they opened the door, rolled up the stairs and I got off the plane. I asked what this was all about, but no one was speaking. They drove me to the Red Cross Building on the Main Post and directed me into the office. When I entered the Red Cross Director stood up when I entered his office and asked me to be seated.

'Sergeant Crocker,' he began, 'our Red Cross Office in San Diego has just notified us that your mother in San Diego has passed away and your presence is required there.' How could that be, I said to myself. I had just left her a couple of days ago and she was feeling just great.

'There must be some mistake,' I said. He handed me the telegram, but I didn't read it. With all the things that were going around in my head, it was most difficult to make one single thought stop and stand still. This sort of thing just doesn't happen to you but always to someone else. You know that from your childhood forward. It just doesn't happen to you. Besides, she promised to bake me some chocolate chip cookies and send them to me in Turkey for Christmas. What silly little thoughts go through your head when logic has taken flight.

'Sergeant Crocker . . . Sergeant Crocker.'

'Yes,'

'If you hurry along now, you will be able to get a flight to the coast out of Idlewild this afternoon. It should get you home around midnight.'

'Thank you,' I think I said, but I couldn't be sure. A staff car was provided and they got me to the airport in ample time to get my flight. We were told that we had two stops for fuel, one in Chicago and the other being Albuquerque, New Mexico.

We were twenty minutes late taking off from New York but were told that we should make up time en route. In my mental situation, what was twenty minutes one way or the other. When we reached Albuquerque, we had a thirty minute stopover for re-fuelling. I decided to call White Sands Proving Grounds and try to get hold of Herb and let him know what had happened. As luck would have it, when I called the Orderly Room Herb had just come in and took the call immediately. He too was as shocked as I was and told me that he would speak to General Hall in the morning.

Uncle Harry met me at the airport and took me home. On the way, he filled me in on what had been taking place and gave me some idea of just what I had to do. I thanked Uncle Harry and told him that I would see him in the morning.

About 3.00 p.m. the next afternoon, Herb phoned me and told me that he had spoken to General Hall and he had given him three days off to come out to California to help me. I told him to thank the General very much and that I appreciated what he had done.

I opened my eyes around 6.30 a.m. and decided to get up and pull myself together and screw my head back on correctly as there was very much to be accomplished. There was some instant coffee in the cupboard so I made do for the time being. First I made a grocery list, as after all I did have to eat. Next came the thoughts of people to ride in the family car. After a process of elimination I finally licked that problem. The floral piece for the casket would be made of her favourite flowers, carnations. After I returned from the grocery store I'll take up the problems of the administrative details. You know, cancel Class F Government allotment which Mum Hazel received, and return same back to the government. Check with the Funeral Home to ensure that all required forms have been completed and processed. Check the official Funeral Service Programme to ensure that dates and names are correct and a number of other things. The list just seems to go on. However, since this is a government funeral, all details must be correct. I had better be off to the store or Herb will arrive and there won't be much to eat here in the house.

As I was returning home when I saw Herb's bright yellow De Soto pull up at our home on Congress Street. He saw me and came over to help me with the groceries.

'Hi Carl old boy, how are you holding up?'

'Just go easy on that 'old' stuff. To answer your question, not too badly considering everything. Frankly Herb, I just haven't got the time to sit down and cry my heart out. Roger and Jim, my brothers, have done what they could but in matters like this, they are just plain hopeless. I guess my three months duty at Fort Worth, Texas General Depot, returning World War II dead home to their parents and families has given me a slight edge in matters like these, even for my own mum. When everything is accomplished and she is laid to rest, then it will be my turn to cry my heart out by myself. Until then there is a lot of work to be accomplished.'

Since it was an early morning funeral, I had sandwiches and little sweet cakes with coffee and tea for those who wanted it. Next, I put on the stereo and had some of her favourite music playing softly. Some of the handkerchief brigade seemed a little shocked at the morning setting in our home. Mum Hazel was not a person who liked gloom and crying, so I tried to have things the way I thought she would like to have them. I was criticized for my actions, but after all, whose mother's funeral was it? Since I knew her better than most, I did what I thought she would like. If the rest of them didn't like it, well, it was just too damn bad. Three days later, Herb departed and left for his return to White Sands Proving Grounds. I sent a letter back with him thanking General Hall and the many people who sent flowers.

Two days later I called my two brothers together to see how we were going to pay over $4,000 over and above the money that the government had allowed for the funeral. Roger stated that his job was very low paying and he just managed to keep himself and make payments on his vehicle. Understandable. Jim stated that he had his family to look after and he just couldn't help. Again, understandable. In short, I would be left to come to some arrangement to pay the doctors, hospital and funeral home on my Staff Sergeant's pay. Agreements were made with all three factors and each would receive a quarter of my monthly pay until the debt was fully paid. However, I learned six weeks later after I had started paying off the debt, Jim was able to come up with enough money to put down on a new family home.

With my time running out at home, I finally got myself busy and baked myself some chocolate chip cookies, packed and mailed them so I would have something coming for Christmas. When all was complete, I had Uncle Harry drive me to the airport and I was on my way back to McGuire Air Force Base, in New Jersey.

It was a couple of days before a flight was scheduled for Germany. The weather was getting a bit cold and we had a few flakes of snow. When Friday morning rolled around, the sky looked ominous so far as flying was concerned. Be that as it may, we were all out of our barracks and ready for boarding our buses to the aircraft loading area. The buses arrived and in no time at all we were all loaded onto the aircraft. Being a C-54 aircraft there was ample leg room. The wait was short lived as they started the engines with a bellow of blue white smoke which seemed to engulf the entire wing for a few seconds. Shortly, all four engines were humming along and we started to move down the runway. Faster and faster we travelled and then we were airborne heading east out over the Atlantic Ocean. Our first scheduled stop is Gander Air Force Base, Newfoundland, Canada. At that point we will take on all the fuel the C-54 can hold and then head out over the North Atlantic Ocean towards Ireland. Coming into Gander we are in a damn heavy snow storm and bouncing around like a ball. As you look around, you don't see too many people engaged in conversation as most I'm sure are further engaged in serious prayers. With a short break in the weather I can see that the ground is coming up to meet us which gives you the feeling that the pilot is coming in for a landing. For many of the young men this is their first time flying and it really shows.'Hey Serg.' one soldier calls to me. 'Can you tell me what this little brown bag is for?'

'It's like this soldier, they put it in the pocket in front of you just in case you lose some of your personal belongings during the flight.'

'That's a stupid statement Sergeant.'

'Is it? Let me say in my defence. Time is a great teller of truth.' As we touch down the snow is flying past our windows a mile a minute. We are down safely and a lot can be said about that in any language. A voice comes over the inter-com stating that we are in Gander, Newfoundland and we'll be on the ground until such time as the storm lets up. There is a canteen in the terminal and that is where the bus will be taking us. We are told to remain there until our flight is called. So far so good.

Three and a half hours later we get the news that we are to get aboard the bus and return to the aircraft. Once loaded and engines started, we taxi down the runway. At a roaring clip, we are now heading out over the North Atlantic Ocean with our nose pointing towards Ireland. At this point all I can say is that I hope Saint Christopher hasn't gone on vacation and will be looking in on us from time to time during our flight to Ireland.

'Hey Serg, what did that man mean when he said that he had reached the point of no return?'

'Let me put it to you another way. What he was saying is that it will be just as far to swim in the direction we are going as it would be to try and swim back from where we have just come. In short, we are half way there.'

Morning had broken when I opened my eyes and it was a clear day. In the distance I could see what I thought was land. My first thought was thank God the navigator stayed up all night to get us across the North Atlantic Ocean and that must be Ireland in the distance. This was confirmed a few minutes later when the announcement came over the inter-com stating that we were due to land at Shannon Airport in about twenty minutes.

Time passed rather quickly and we were soon back on the plane heading for Frankfurt, Germany. Frankfurt seemed just a hop skip and a jump away from Shannon Airport and we were there seemingly in no time at all. When we arrived in Frankfurt, we were taken by military buses to a holding station awaiting onward transportation to Turkey via Commercial Air. With my emergency leave back to San Diego, plus my various waiting times getting to Germany, Christmas was just three days away. There was no way any of us could get to our assignments prior to Christmas. Looking around, I could see that the young soldiers in my Squad Room were really deflated and really homesick. Looking around you could see a few red eyes here and there as these young men had never been far away from home during the holidays. Putting my current personal loss to one side, I had to come up with a foolproof plan to get their minds off of their being homesick. Further, at this point it seemed that they were old enough to let them take charge of their own lives.

'I'm Sergeant Crocker and what are your names?'

'Just call me Jim,' 'I'm Alfred,' 'Me? I'm Michael and this is George.' 'And I'm Alex.'

'Pleased to meet all of you. I have a question to let you guys kick around to see if you want to celebrate Christmas or just lie around, be miserable, and let Christmas pass you by. Whatever you decide, I'll be back in ten minutes to find out what you all would like to do.'

I went to the Mess Hall to see the Mess Sergeant to see what if anything he could give us just in case they decided to have Christmas in our Squad Room. Upon my return, they voted unanimously to celebrate Christmas and seemed happy about it.

'Now let's get ourselves organised as there isn't too much time at hand. Okay, George, get all of our names and place them on a piece of paper. When that is accomplished we'll all draw out names. Should you draw your own name, put it back and draw out another. Once you have a name, you will go to the Military Post Exchange and purchase a gift of around $2.00 and have it wrapped. By that time I should be able to come up with a Christmas Tree and you can place the gift under the tree. George, go over and see the Mess Sergeant and tell him that Sergeant Crocker sent you. I saw him earlier and he stated that he could come up with something for us.'

'Good show Serg.'

'Alex, go and see if you can get some Christmas candy from the Women's Group over by the Chapel. The Chaplain told me he had several Christmas trees and if we wanted one we were certainly welcome to it. He also said that he had a few decorations we could use on our tree. See, things are really falling in place. Michael, maybe you can get some cake from the Enlisted Men's Club. However, just be sure you bring it back and not eat it on the way. I wonder what Jim and Alfred have come up with? I'm sure that they won't come home empty handed.'

'Just look at our tree.'

'Yea, Serg, but look what we have under the tree. There are oranges, nuts of all kinds, cake, Christmas candy, not to mention the gifts under the tree.'

'I don't know about you men, but I think I will be going to the Protestant Christmas Eve Service at the Post Chapel. If any of you want to come you're more than welcome.'

'What do you say Serg if we all go?'

'That will be great and we can have our Christmas Party after

24

church. I'll say once again, that our little tree and the presents under it sure makes it feel more like Christmas and not just an empty day. I feel sure in years to come we'll look back and reflect on the positive interaction we all played.'

'You know Serg, this is the first time I've ever been in church on a Christmas Eve in my life.'

'George, I guess you noted one thing above all.'

'What was that Serg?'

'The roof didn't fall in on you.'

'Get off my back Serg.'

'Just joking. It was a very nice service.'

'By the way Serg, who is going to play Santa Claus?'

'I believe each of us will play Santa Claus and give our gifts to one another.'

'Good thinking Serg.'

'First, here are some cookies that the Mess Sergeant threw in for good measure.'

'Not bad at all.'

'Okay Alex, you'll be the first Santa Claus and select any present with the name on the package.'

'Here's one and it's for Michael.'

'What did you get Michael?'

'Just a minute. Ah, it's a deck of Kim Playing Cards. Not bad.'

'Okay Michael, you select a package.'

'Here's one and it is for George.'

'It's a shoe shine kit and something I really needed. Thanks.'

'Now you select George.'

'Let's see. Here's one and it looks like it's for Alex.'

'I've always needed one of these. What is it?'

'It's a good sewing kit but there is no woman enclosed to do the sewing.'

'What in the hell did you want Alex for $2.00 something?'

'Alex, you select.'

'This one is for you Jim.'

'Good show, it's a nail clipper set.'

'Select Jim. There are two gifts left, so one must be for Serg or Alfred.'

'Alfred, it's yours.'

'Say, this is a nice black address book which I'm sure will be put to good use before I leave Europe.'

'Okay Alfred, hand Serg his gift. Serg, before you open your gift, let me say, we all chipped in and got you your present as it had to be something a little special for showing us that Christmas is where the heart is and sharing it with others. Thanks Serg.' Opening the box I see that it's a good brand of stationery with my initials engraved in gold at the top.

'Men, for me to say that you shouldn't have done it would be a waste of words and energy, but I accept it gracefully and thank you all very kindly.'

Christmas Day was spent walking around Frankfurt seeing the sights and taking a few pictures. Later we all returned to the Consolidated Mess where we had a beautiful Christmas Dinner with all the trimmings. The following day, Alex, George, Jim, Alfred and Michael were all shipped out to their new duty stations somewhere in Europe. I was left in Frankfurt by myself awaiting my on forwarding transportation to Ankara, Turkey. I didn't have long to wait as I was informed that I would be leaving the following day. They further told me that I would be leaving on Royal Dutch Airlines (KLM) for Istanbul. After that, I would transfer to the Turkish Airlines (THY) for transportation on to Ankara.

With the arrival of Thursday morning, not too much sleep Wednesday night as the excitement took over. By 10.00 hours I was at the Frankfurt International Airport with my ticket and travel orders in hand and ready to board the KLM Flight to Istanbul. Oh God, while waiting here, I suddenly have to go to the toilet. I just wonder if they are going to call the flight to load while I'm in letting my bladder relax. If they do, they will just have to wait until I'm finished and that's all there is to it. I feel much better now, and no, they haven't called for the flight to start loading. Shortly, the light goes on and we are told that KLM Flight (whatever number it was) was ready for loading. I had my boarding pass, my passport, ticket and some other papers in my hand. What I didn't notice was that one of the papers in my hand was the United States Government Rating paper to make an assessment on how KLM treated US Military personnel travelling on their airlines. The chief hostess spotted the paper in my hand and in one quick flash I was seated in Business Class with all the extras. At first I thought that I was just plain lucky, but I should have known that something was up. It was almost like being in First Class. It wasn't until I settled down and started reading the extra papers in my ticket folder did I fully understand why I was receiving all this special attention. With a good report from me and others, Uncle Sam would be using KLM on all special trips out of Frankfurt, Germany. Pretty clever these Dutchmen.

Winging our way over Europe, we land in Rome at Leonardo Da Vinci Airport. I got off, had a look around, got back on and before too long we were on our way to Istanbul. It seemed like a rather short trip, to what I had pictured in my mind, and before long we landed at Yesilköy Airport in Istanbul. We must have landed out in the sticks as I didn't see anything that even looked like a city or even a small village. As I look around I see two other US Military Personnel in the same KLM area. Shortly, a man comes up to our area and tells us that our mini bus is waiting for us to take us to the Park Hotel in downtown Istanbul. When we get settled, the first thing I'm going to have is a good cup of coffee and kick off my shoes.

As we start our trip into the city, I seem to see strange things lurking up from our countryside and they look like missile installations. There are some over there and even more over there. As we draw closer to the city I see more and more sights. Knowing that Turkey is one of NATO's staunchest supporters, I didn't think that they would have their missiles exposed to the outside world in such a way as they do. In the States our missiles are for the most part underground. Not so here in Turkey. They are exposed to the elements day in and day out. When I raised the question about their exposed missiles sites, I was politely told that they were not missiles sites, but rather minarets attached to a mosque. Did I feel stupid? You know the answer. Further down the road from the airport, we start to pass a few people here and there. There also seem to be a few more buildings. As I was straining my neck to see what type of structure we were passing. I was informed it was an aqueduct which was built during the time when Rome and it's legions ruled this area. Having survived the test of time, it now stands most majestically and most impressive. As you look further, you can see where once stood a great wall which protected the city. Like everything else, time and erosion has taken a heavy toll on this structure. Parts of the wall seem to be nearly level with the surrounding earth. You can only imagine in your wildest thoughts what must have transpired during this period of history. Great armies and great leaders of that period came fought and died here. But time proved to be the final victor overall. As we travel this road and from this vantage point you can start to see the vast city of Istanbul which spreads out far and wide and crosses two continents, both Europe and Asia.

Further, when you start or try to envision just how old this land is you will have to go back some 2,000 years BC to the time of the Hittites. That in itself is very difficult to comprehend. We can only hope that we do. However, crossing into modern day Turkey's history you would find such names as Cyrus of Persia, Alexander the Great, Constantine I of Rome, and we have only reached the 11th century in the time of the Seljuk Turks. Truly, this country has had a most difficult but glorious past with history of which few have ever taken the time to learn.

Now we are entering into a part of the city with vehicles, horse drawn wagons and people cramming the streets and going in all directions. Horns blowing, people shouting while selling their wares, men walking arm and arm, pigeons flying to and fro, push carts blocking roads, all seem to be part of the everyday life in this vast and colourful city they call Istanbul.

With more and more traffic as we enter what which seems like the centre of the city we arrive at the Park Hotel. The hotel sets sort of off the main beat from a section of the city called Taksim and down a little side street which leads from the main part of the city centre. Your first impression of the Park Hotel is that it's a nice little hotel. Lovely gardens greet you upon entering. However, once inside the grounds of the hotel it is much larger than your first impression. Our bags were brought in as we made our way to the Reception Desk. With a smile, we were handed forms to fill out. When that was completed, we were then asked for our Passports. Why in hell do they want our passports, as we went through Customs and Immigration at the airport.

'Why do you require our passports I enquired?'

'Well Sir, there is information that our police require on all persons entering into Turkey.'

'I have another question. The information which is required, is it for the Civil Police or for the Secret Police?'

'Sir, I cannot answer that question.'

'It was stupid of me to even ask that question in the first place, wasn't it.'

'I'll answer that question, yes it was. Sir, this gentleman will show you to your room.'

'Thank you.'

After a hot shower, I'm ready to take on the world. Well, maybe not the world, but a good cup of coffee. Down to the lounge I go, seeking out a waiter, and order myself a nice cup of coffee. Of course, I didn't catch what the waiter said, but I nodded okay. Soon, this nice little cup of coffee was placed in front of me, and was steaming hot. Trying to look cosmopolitan, sophisticated and not to mention refined, I picked up my cup of coffee and took one big swig. Oh my God, what have I done? I suddenly realise not only do I have a mouth full of coffee, but also a mouth full of coffee grounds as well. What in the hell do I do now? Should I spit it back into the cup, swallow it gracefully, or head for the nearest potted plant over in the far corner? Heading towards the potted plant I see a black silhouette of a man followed by WC and know that I've found the Men's Room just in the nick of time. With my mouth washed out and my dignity once again restored, I head back to the lounge and that nasty little cup of coffee which was the source of my embarrassment. Sitting on the chair, I laugh at myself and realise that every day there is something new to be learned. Today, it was Turkish coffee, and how not to drink it. Tomorrow? who knows.

Chapter Three

It looks like it's snowing again with the wind blowing up a nasty storm. There goes our night sightseeing trip for tonight. We'll be leaving for Ankara tomorrow and there should be plenty of time to see Istanbul at a later date. I was going to the Iş Bank just up the street to change some green backs into some Turkish lira. As I think about it, I surely don't want to go out into this snowstorm the way it's blowing now. On the other hand, if I don't change it here, I most likely can get it at Yesilköy Airport before taking off for Ankara. Not to worry, as I have sixty-five Turkish lira for tonight's dinner plus a small tip for the waiter which should tide me over until tomorrow.

'Sir, your transportation is now ready to take you to the airport. Here is your Passport, and your luggage will be brought down from your room. We hope that you have enjoyed your stay here in Istanbul. At a later date should you return to Istanbul, we hope that you will stay with us.'

'Thank you.'

They must have had one hell of a snowstorm last night as they are still trying to clear it off the roads. Using thatch brooms to clear the snow is a very difficult job in anyone's language. I guess you use what you have and just be thankful that you have it. Looking skywards, the weather still looks ominous and not too promising. After a flat tyre, and a number of well chosen words by our Turkish driver, we were once again on the road to the airport. Snow was still tumbling down but not as heavy as it was before. On arrival at the airport we checked in with THY (Turkish Airlines) and were informed that there would be a slight delay. It's now 2.00 p.m. on Friday afternoon so there is plenty of time for my military sponsor to be alerted and meet me in Ankara at Esenböga Airport. He'll have time to get me settled in Ankara prior to my In Processing in JAMMAT. Here comes another announcement in Turkish about some airline but I can't understand a word they are saying. I had better check with THY counter to see if it was our flight. Yes, I'm told, we'll be delayed until further notice as it is snowing pretty heavily in Ankara at the present time. In that case, I had better look for the place that changes money from dollars into Turkish lira. Back to the THY counter I go to ask them where the place is for Foreign Exchange.

'Excuse me Sir, can you tell me where the Foreign Exchange Office is located?'

'It is just down there.'

'Thank you Sir.'

'Just one minute Sir, since we are not expecting any more International Flights in today, the Foreign Exchange personnel have closed and have gone home for the day. Oh shit. I only have 5.00 Turkish lira and I'm beginning to get that sinking feeling in my stomach. Oh well, I'm sure that my military sponsor will have the situation covered when I get to Ankara, so I won't worry.

It is now 4.30 p.m. and they still haven't called our flight. It is starting to get dark outside and I sure hope they know what they are doing. To be on the safe side, I've located myself just across from the THY counter just in case they call our flight. A few minutes later, the man behind the THY counter motioned for me to come to the counter.

'We'll be loading in five minutes for Ankara. Please have your carry on luggage and your ticket ready as they have completed de-icing the aircraft.'

As we move forward towards the gate, the weather still seems rather dark and forbidding as it was earlier in the afternoon. I surely hope they fully know what they are doing. We have reached the end of the runway without being called back so it's reasonable to assume that come hell or high water, in this case snow, we are going to take off. The one thing I do take comfort from is the fact that we are flying in a C-47 which is an excellent aircraft. On the other hand, I really can't vouch for the crew and its members. Since we have taken off, I can only pray that the Gods will get us to our destination safely and soundly . . . Amen. Looking across the aisle, the Air Force Sergeant that's on board with me seems a little white around the gills, so to speak. I would feel much better if this bouncing around would end. Nearly an hour has passed and we seem to be heading down as my ears are beginning to pop when I open my mouth. In the distance, I believe I'm beginning to see some lights and my spirits are beginning to lighten up a wee bit. It must be . . . it just has to be. I think I can see blue and amber lights which would indicate it must be a runway. Yep, that's a runway down there and I pray that it's Ankara. The lights flash on inside the aircraft which reads in English and Turkish (Fasten Seat Belts – No Smoking Please) I sure hope that I haven't kept my Military Sponsor waiting too long for me here at the Airport. The guy must be really tired after all this waiting for me to arrive. Thank God, it's all over now. As we make our way into the terminal I can only see one Air Force NCO who would appear like he is waiting for someone. Since I'm Army and he is Air Force I somehow have a feeling that he isn't waiting for me. My sponsor must be here somewhere. Maybe he had to relieve himself and has gone to the toilet. Surely, he wouldn't leave me here to fend for myself . . . would he?'

'Excuse me Sergeant, but have you seen an Army Sergeant here in the terminal waiting for anyone?'

'There was one Army Sergeant here about two hours ago, but he left and went back into town. When he left, he said that the person he was waiting for flight had been cancelled from Istanbul.'

'Did he say anything else?'

'Oh yea, he said that he was tired of waiting and since the flight had been cancelled that he was going to a party in Ankara and if by chance you should arrive, he hoped someone would be able to direct me to the Tourist Hotel.'

'Did he say anything else?'

'No, he left and drove away in a Staff Car.'

'I'll be a son-of-a-bitch.'

Obviously the party must have been more important than checking with the THY officials to verify the arrival of our flight from Istanbul.

'As you can guess, I'm the one left holding the bag.'

'It sure looks like you have a problem, doesn't it.'

'One might just say that. However, I just have the JAMMAT Telephone number and I'll just give them a call.'

'Good luck.' I go to the THY counter and ask the young man there if it is possible to use his phone. He smiles at me and pushes the phone over to me. I lift the receiver and I hear a Turkish lady saying something. I can only assume that she is asking me for my number. Quickly,

I hand the telephone back to the THY Staff and show him the number that I want. He tells the operator the number and then hands the telephone back to me. On the other end of the line is a person speaking Turkish. Shit, that doesn't do me one damn bit of good. I hand the telephone back to the THY man. After a short conversation he hung up the phone. He turns to me and states that there are no American personnel currently present in the headquarters. That's damn funny to me, as there is supposed to be a Duty Officer and a Duty NCO. Maybe, they do things differently here. I'm beginning to become a bit concerned for my own well being. As the Air Force Sergeant starts to leave, I ask him, 'Do you go by the Tourist Hotel in downtown Ankara?'

'Just by chance we do Sergeant.'

'I don't suppose you would mind taking another person with you, would you?'

'Not at all.'

As we start to leave the airport, it starts to snow once again. The slow drive into the city at a snail's pace, it took about one hour.

We arrived at the Tourist Hotel and I got my luggage out of the trunk of the car and thanked the Sergeant. Apprehensively, I made my way into the lobby and to the reception desk. The strong smell of Turkish cigarette smoke filled the lobby and seemed to be emanating from the coffee room just opposite the lobby. My God, what a stench. As I move closer to the reception desk I start to get that real sinking feeling once again. No, oh no, no, they don't speak any English and I'm faced with this strange sounding language once again. Maybe, just maybe, I'll be better this time with my sign language and won't have to resort to drawing pictures once again. The manager, or whoever he is just gave me a form to fill out which is in Turkish and French. I've been screwed up before, but this beats the holy hell out of me. I'll just put my name on the form and my military address and hope they can take it from there. Before I give these people my passport in this hotel, I had better write it down just to ensure what the number is just in case they should lose it . . . or sell it. It's a special passport number 264480 issued in Washington DC. There, I now have a record of the number just in case. Yes, he took my passport. It seems that I do have a reservation in this hotel, why, I don't know. He looks at me, I look at him, and this little game lasts for about fifteen seconds. I guess I must have passed the look test.

After all the formalities had been completed, I was handed a key which read 440. There was no elevator to transport my luggage or myself up four flights of stairs to Room 440. With my duffel bag and a suite case that was more than enough thank you. Porters? Never heard of them. Reaching the room, I can see that it's on the western side and the room is cold as hell. Shortly a young boy comes up and turns on the steam heat. Through the window with no curtains, I can see that it has started to snow once again. Standing next to the heater with my overcoat on, I'm still cold. With all the bouncing around I did on the aeroplane and waiting at the airport, I had better find the little boy's room. Looking around, I can see that the toilet is nowhere to be found in my room. It must be located in the hallway. Ah yes, there's that sign again (WC). I entered the room and opened one of the doors. Holy shit, I closed the door faster than I opened it. What a stinking, rotten, filthy, shitty smell came forth. Not only that, but my eyes started to water as the stench was so strong. I would even go so far as to state that this was far worse than Joyce's wind breaking ceremony at White Sands Proving Ground a few months back. Needless to say I made an extremely fast exit from that room and returned to my room to think this situation out. As I recall, I didn't see any regular or normal western type toilet in the little room when I opened the door. What I did see was a slab of marble raised about six inches off of the floor and a place to put your two feet. The slab of marble is about three feet across and about four feet deep. The four corners are bevelled, sloping towards the back. A five inch diameter hole has been placed in the marble towards the back which coincides with the place to place your two feet. Just what in the hell that was supposed to be I'll never know. I do know however, that it was one stinking place. Logic tells me to check the other floors on the opposite side of the hotel to see if the conditions persist. Having my doubts, I proceeded to the third floor on the opposite side of the hotel and enter the (WC). Opening the door marked (WC Toilet) I find once again this strange looking thing and a place to put your two feet. The smell is slight and nothing like I found on the fourth floor. Entering this thing that is marked as a toilet I place my feet on the marble pedestal which is carved like a pair of shoes and stand there. As a little kid would say, 'I accomplished No.1, teacher.' As I see it, the next controlled strategic movement is going to be far more sophisticated and complicated than first anticipated. Again, like the little kid said to his teacher, 'Hey teacher, I have to do Number 2.' Now, what do I do, and how do I do it? Do I stand up to do it? Do I bend down and take off my pants and underpants to do it? If so, now what do I do about my shoes? Do I take them off as well? By the time that I get this controlled strategic movement figured out, it will be time to send my clothing out to be washed. I'm missing a very important factor in this operation. Where in the hell is the toilet paper. Now this could present a very big problem as they do not have any Sears Catalogues hanging about. This entire operation reminds me of a bombardier during World War II when he was on his bombing mission. That is, peeping down the bomb sight, he has to aim to see that which he is about to release is going straight down to hit its target. Shit, I missed. With no toilet paper, Sears Catalogue or Kleenex at my disposal, I'm about to become unglued with the realisation of what I'm now faced with. I see a little faucet by my right foot and wonder just what part it is to play in this strategic movement. After ten minutes of applied logic, while in the squatting position, I finally reached the verdict as to what the water faucet played. This little water faucet by your right foot which is used to wash that which you have just used. That's right, just what you have used. However, you are sure in real strife if you are left handed. I'm well aware that life was never meant to be really easy, but by the same token this controlled strategic movement is just ridiculous and damn nerve racking to perform. Talk about your cultural shocks, hell, I'm going to have to be potty trained all over again. For certain, I'm lucky that I wasn't faced with a case of Montezuma's Revenge or I would have been faced with a massive clean up project. However, there is one very important thing I'm going to have to learn and that is how to balance myself in the squatting position with my feet on the marble foot pedestals and complete that which I went there to do. Should I be able to accomplish that balancing act, I'm sure that Barnum and Bailey Circus would be more than happy to hire me. As I climb the stairs up to the fourth floor, the people in Room 437 seem to be having a hot sex orgy. As I look through the partly open door I can see that she is on top of him and both of them are stark naked screwing up a storm. Upon further investigation I don't know if it would be called an open door policy or an invitation to join them. However, I can't say too much about my military sponsor for booking me into this hotel. I can't help wondering just what kind of a person he must be to have placed me here. Oh no, he's on top of her and she is groaning loud and clear. I don't think that they are locals, as they both have blonde hair and seem like speaking German, Dutch or Danish. Anyway, it's a good live show, but as much as I would like to stay and see the finish of this production it appears that there is water running from under the door in my room. Oh shit there is water all over the floor and it is coming from the steam heater. If I had a return air ticket, I would leave right now. Down to the reception desk I find myself once again. Now I find myself in one hell of a dilemma as to how I'm going to tell the manager that I have a pretty big problem in my room with the water running everywhere. Taking the pencil on his desk and some paper I start to draw a picture of what is happening in my room. I'm dead serious. At this point the manager smiles at me and utters something in Turkish. He takes the pencil from me and he too starts to draw pictures. For God's sake, he hasn't got a clue as to what I'm trying to tell him. I take the pencil once again and draw my room and place the room number 440 on the door. He smiles, takes the pencil once again and draws the pattern for Tic Tac Toe. At this point I yell 'NO, NO.' His eyes narrow and he gives me a very stern look and seems to be getting irritated with me and my actions. What a hopeless feeling I have by not being able to express myself on a matter of urgency. In sheer desperation I grabbed the bottle of drinking water and poured it on his desk. To say that he had gotten upset would be a mild statement. I then took the pencil out of his hand and wrote Room 440, pointing at me. A real puzzled look crossed his face and he called one of the employees to help solve my riddle. I started upstairs and motioned for them to follow me. With a smile from both of them they rejected my invitation. A young boy in the office, he could have been the owner's son, could see that I was very troubled so he motioned that he would go upstairs with me. His father said something in Turkish and the boy just looked at him. When we got to the room and I had opened the door, he could see that I had a serious problem. He said something to me in Turkish and dashed back downstairs. Shortly, I heard something like a herd of wild cattle come rushing up the stairs. By this time, my room resembled the mighty muddy Mississippi River with the main channel running right down the middle of my room and started to overflow its banks. Panic was written all over their faces as the water started running into the hallway. Me? I could have cared less, as it was after all, their room, their water and their hotel. The moaning and groaning in Room 437 gave way to the shouting and yelling going on in Room 440. Shortly, the man in Room 437 came to his doorway with a towel wrapped around him and was now viewing my open door action. My situation wasn't nearly as mind boggling as his open door sex orgy. In a way they both had something in common. That is, all the yelling and shouting taking place. The one thing I can safely say without any hesitation, is that my brief stay in Ankara so far, has been anything but dull. I pray God that this is not an omen of things to come.

After an hour or so, they finally repaired the steam heater and departed my room. They sent up an old woman to clean up the mess they had made and to mop the floor. Poor old soul, she could hardly push the mop from one place to another. I thought for a while she expected me to do it. Truly, my heart went out to her, but after having run up and down the four flights of stairs so far this evening plus the fact that I haven't had anything to eat, I too am beginning to feel the pinch. Trying not to be mean or too disrespectful, but the old dear sort of looks like the Whistler's Mother once or twice removed. When she smiled, and she did once, her missing teeth and the way she had her hair wrapped up reminded me of the French Revolution with the old hags shouting when the guillotine came down and lopped off a head, and they would knit one pearl two. It has taken about thirty-five minutes for her to complete her work here in my room and the old dear looks like she is beat. Well, I figure that makes two of us. She closed the door and said something in Turkish. I smiled and let it go at that. My God, it's now 11.45 p.m. I'm tired and hungry but I think I'll call it a night, a rotten one at that.

At 6.30 a.m. I'm up, dressed and heading downstairs to see if my 5 Turkish lira can get me anything to eat or drink. As I enter the little restaurant (the sign reads in Turkish Lokanta) I see some round bread looking thing with sesame seeds on top and they look and smell pretty good. I pointed and the young man brought me one. I made in sign language a motion like I wanted something to drink. Shortly he returns with something that looks like tea in a glass with two lumps of sugar on the side in a saucer. I handed him my 5 lira note and he soon returned bringing me 4 lira and 50 kurus. At this going rate, I can have the same thing for lunch, and dinner and still have money left over. When you have so little money of their type of currency you can't expect to have a juicy fillet of steak and all the trimmings.

The sun has broken through the clouds which has taken some of the gloom off of this place, so maybe I'll go for a walk. The street sweepers are all wrapped up to keep warm as they swing their thatch brooms sweeping the snow off of the sidewalk and into the gutters. From my observation, the brooms seem to be working and the job getting done. You can't ask more than that. My God, would you look at that over there. There go two men in military uniforms walking down the street in broad daylight arm in arm. Glancing across the street I see two more military men doing the same thing. What kind of a no no land have I landed in? I just wonder what our military authorities would have to say on this subject. I bet it would be damn explosive and cause one hell of a cry throughout the land. I'm sure many would like to try it, but modesty would compel them to refuse. Damn modesty. After having said that, who gives a poop. This is their country and they can damn well do what they want. Far be it for me to raise my eyebrow.

Saturday and Sunday passed rather quickly without too much to do. Went out several times, but didn't venture too far from the hotel. Since this is Monday, I should be meeting my sponsor before too long. Sitting here, I'm just debating if I should say something about this hotel or just let it ride. If he is smaller than me, I'll tell him. On the other hand, if he is bigger than me, I'll just let it pass for the time being. I'll find the right time and place to sock it to him.

A staff car pulls up in front of the hotel and a Sergeant who is about 6' 2" tall and about 230 lbs steps out. It must be Sergeant Morris. Not to show him that I was happy to see him, I let him come into the hotel and seek me out. He comes over to me and asks are you Sergeant Crocker? I could have given him a rather smart answer, as I was the only US Sergeant in uniform sitting in the lobby.

'Yes, I'm Sergeant Crocker.'

'I'm Sergeant Morris.'

'I had gathered that much.'

'I was expecting to meet you on Friday evening when I arrived from Istanbul.'

'By the way, how was the party?'

'It sounds like you are a little pissed off at me from the sound in your voice.'

'What on earth would ever give you such an idea? Let's skip it now Sergeant Morris, as it is past history.'

'Well, shall we leave for JAMMAT and get checked in?'

'It's okay with me.'

'By the way, how is the hotel?'

'I just as soon you didn't ask.' Now, it wasn't that I was being bitchy, but my sponsor didn't impress me either. I felt the less I had to do with him, the better.

'That's our headquarters building over there.' I looked in the direction he was pointing and what I saw looked like a building from the Mediaeval period. The only things that seemed lacking were moats and the drawbridge. To this point in time, I'm not too impressed. Things just have to get better was the thought that crossed my mind.

'Sergeant Crocker, before you start your in processing, would you care for a cup of coffee? I'm buying.'

'Then lead me to it. Needless to say, that's the most intelligent thing I've heard all morning.' As we enter the snack bar, there seems to be a handful of people there slurping their morning coffee. I find out later, that the more noise you make, the better it is supposed to be. After we obtain ours, Sergeant Morris leads us to a table where a woman is seated. 'Hi Joyce', he addresses her, 'this is Sergeant Crocker who just arrived and will be going out to Erzurum.'

'Hi Sergeant Crocker, I'm Joyce Backhouse, and I work in the office.'

'She's being modest, Sergeant Crocker, she runs this place and we all know it. If she ever left JAMMAT, the whole damn place would fall flat on its face.'

'After all that, I guess I had better head back to my office.'

'Most pleased to have met you.'

'See you later Joyce.'

'Welcome to the Mission, Sergeant Crocker.'

'Thanks.'

'By the way, do I have time for another cup of coffee before I start my In Processing?'

'Sure, you can even have a donut if it strikes your fancy.'

'Now that you have mentioned it, a couple of donuts would hit the spot.'

'Would you care for anything besides coffee while I'm up?'

'No, coffee will suffice.'

'Here we are.'

By the way, what is on our agenda for today?'

'We will have to go to the Turkish General Staff Office to obtain your Turkish Military Red Book which gives you official permission to enter the Third Turkish Army Area which is a highly restrictive sector. Without it, you cannot enter that area.'

'I'm told that it is rather cold out in that area.'

'Cold you say, it will freeze the balls off a brass monkey in less than it would to take to spell E R Z U R U M.'

'That's pretty cold.'

'If you are finished, we can go upstairs and get you signed into the headquarters and get you officially enrolled in JAMMAT.'

'When do you anticipate I'll complete my processing and be heading out East to Erzurum? At this point in time, I have had enough of living out of my suite case and duffel bag and would like to get settled.'

'Should all go well, it could be as early as Wednesday or Thursday. By the way, after today's processing what do you have planned for tonight?'

'Being new in town, not much of anything.'

'If you are interested, they have a new belly dancer at the Gar Casino. It is a floor show and dinner and it's not too expensive. Do you think you'd be interested?'

'It's probably much better than the current floor show that I have back in Room 437 of my hotel. In Room 437 we have sex-crazed people staying there, with their door partly open so you can watch them.'

'Sounds different to say the least.'

'I look at it this way.'

'What they do is their business just so they don't interfere with me.'

'Well, that sounds reasonable.'

'By the way, if you decide to come, I'll be by at around 8.00 p.m. to pick you up.'

'That sounds okay with me.'

After a day of processing plus using a Western style toilet I feel that I have made progress on my first day in JAMMAT. Not having to use my balancing skill which I have just learned a day or two ago, I'm beginning to feel better about my assignment here. Then again, I had better wait a little longer before I make such a bold statement.

'I see you are right on time Sergeant Morris.'

'After the poor start I made with you on Friday night by not being at the airport, I guess I had better make it up somehow.'

'By the way, what is that building which is all light over to the left sitting on that hill?'

'Oh, that building? It is the Mausoleum of Mustafa Kemal Atatürk the founder of modern day Turkey. History tells us that he was some sort of a guy and really believed in himself and his country. It was a difficult struggle for him and his followers to get Turkey to where it is today.'

'Here we are at the Gar Casino.'

'Nice looking place. Over there where all the lights are is the train station.'

'This place doesn't look too bad.'

'It's not too bad and the prices are reasonable even by our standards.'

'Excuse me Sir, but do you have reservations?'

'Yes, for two, Sergeant Morris.'

'Yes Sergeant Morris, right this way please.' We were led to the left side of the dance floor and seated at a table for two.

'Would you care to order now or would you desire a drink first?'

'Would you please bring us the wine list?'

'Here in Turkey, they have great wine. And excellent wine is the Kavaklidere selections. They have Yakut Damlasi, Äankayi Yildizi, Ankara Kimizi Dîmisek, Tatli and Lal. Now having said all that, which do you prefer?'

'Frankly I like Lal.'

'We'll have a bottle of that.'

'Thank you Sir.' As we sit here, the band that is playing seems quite good. 'Where does the belly dancer dance, on the dance floor?'

'No just wait and see.' After a few more selections, the house lights dim and a huge stage rolls right out from under the stage where the band was playing. Suddenly, we find ourselves right next to the stage and have a bird's eye view of everything, and I do mean everything. Slowly a small dim light hits the middle of the stage revealing a beautiful young woman dressed in a white gown with silver sequins glittering in the spotlight. Her gown is very full and flows from her waist to the floor. The upper part of her torso was clad in a loose silver shimmering blouse, further revealing a bear mid section and belly button. The blouse is more like a halter which allows the breasts full play when dancing. Softly the music rings forth with the brass cymbals attached to her thumbs and middle fingers start to pick up the beat. In come the drums with the violins and the instrument called Ut in Turkish. The beat has gotten faster and stronger together with her body movements. At the rate she is moving her hips, buttocks, stomach and her breasts, something is going to come detached and fly across the stage. At the rate she is moving now, she shows no signs of letting up. She is sure in over-drive now. As I look across the room I can see men standing up and starting to go through all sorts of strange gyrations to the beat of the music. It would appear that this haunting beat seems to take over the body in some weird sort of way. As I sit here, it seems that I too want to move my body to the beat of this music. In all fairness, I can say that this young lady is in excellent physical condition because she is still going strong. Watching her go through all her motions seems to give you a compulsion or an irresistible desire to put your body in motion with hers. What a dancer for a young girl. They say she is from Lebanon and that her father and mother travel with her on all her trips. To be sure, they are not far from her side at any given time.

'I think you will also enjoy this next act on the programme.'

'What is it?'

'It's called *The Review de Paris*. All these acts are direct from the Moulin Rouge in Paris. From what I've heard they are just sensational and present some stunning and stimulating acts. Look at the one on this end, I would say that she is the best looking one of the whole lot. Now look at the one on the other end of the line. She is nearly as beautiful as the one at this end.'

'Now Sergeant Morris, which one would you select?'

'Now I don't know.'

'What do you mean you don't know? Aren't you a red-blooded hot American man?'

'Well that's just the problem Carl.'

'What do you mean?'

'So are they.'

'You mean to tell me they are all men?'

'Yes, they are all female impersonators.'

'Well kiss my ass as Fifth and Broadway at high noon.'

In spite of the last development, the dinner was excellent and the service very good.

'What to do you say Sergeant Morris, we finish off this bottle of wine and call it a night.'

'Sounds okay with me.'

'I'll get the check.'

'No, no, I'll get the check as I invited you here for the evening.'

'Okay, so no feelings will be hurt, we'll both pay the check.'

'Okay?'

'Settled.'

Taxi, taxi, yep, he saw us. As I open the door I can smell a very heavy cigarette stench. By the time I get to my hotel I'm positive all my clothing will smell of cigarette smoke. If that's Turkish tobacco, it sure has a very heavy odour.

'Where are you going?' the taxi driver asks in Turkish. Sergeant Morris says, 'Tourist Hotel.' We were off in a flash with squealing tyres and the damn smell of cigarette smoke. In a matter of minutes I'm back in my hotel and I tell Sergeant Morris good night and thank him. As I pass the Reception Desk, I get a friendly smile from the clerk, and return same. Reaching the fourth floor I start to pass Room 437. As I stopped to have another look, you just wouldn't believe what I saw. They are still making love but only this time they have found another man and it's a threesome. Not exaggerating, the new man to join this happy twosome, is standing there stark naked and his male genitals are larger than a donkey on grandfather's farm in all my life, I have never seen anything like that before, and probably will never again. I'm sure I didn't have too much wine. What I saw should be in Ripley's *Believe It Or Not*. As they would say in the (vernacular) brother, he is really hung. However, being as late as it is enough is too much and I'm calling it a night. As I slip off into dream land, I still can hear that fool woman in Room 437 shouting oh no, no, and I can only assume that the third party has started to make his grand entrance. Morning has arrived and it is still very cold. I had to put my overcoat over the top of me last night to try and keep warm. As usual, feeling the heater has proved a waste of time as the damn thing is still cold. Looking out the curtainless window I can see that it is still snowing. From the looks of it, it must have snowed a lot more during the night. After a good glass of hot tea and the world I'm sure will start to look better. As I pass Room 437 on my way downstairs, all seems quiet with no activity taking place. After last night, I'm sure they are all tired after playing one jumps into the cuckoo's nest, not over it. She must be worn to a frazzle . . . poor dear. As I see it, it's their life and their problem and thank God, it's not mine.

There is Sergeant Morris and for once he is on time.

'Good morning, Good morning,'

'Hi there.'

'Well, this should be my last day here in Ankara as I complete my inward processing today and get the train to Erzurum tomorrow.'

'I have made your reservations and will pick up your tickets tomorrow. You will have a private compartment all the way to Erzurum.'

Going out East, I sincerely hope that they will have some heat in the compartment.

Having completed all of my processing and running to the PX for a last few small items, I think that I'm ready to head back to the hotel and call it a day.

'Sergeant Morris, if you don't mind, I think that I'll just have a quiet night and get all my things in order for tomorrow.'

'Not a bad idea Serg, as I have a number of things to accomplish also.'

'Okay, I'll see you in the morning around 9.30 am.

'Sounds like a winner. Thanks for your help today.'

As I make my way up to my hotel room, I pass Room 437, but all is really quiet. It would appear that they have checked out and not before time as far as I'm concerned. Maybe tonight I'll have a complete night's sleep without the sexual cries and groaning. There doesn't seem too much packing to be done now so maybe later I'll make my way down the street to the quaint little Bohemian Restaurant I passed several nights ago.

The appearance as you enter the restaurant would give you the impression of being rather a small place. However, such is not the case. Upon entering a lovely old man greets you with a warm smile and shows you to a table. Freshly cut flowers are protruding from the little vase on each table. In the main part of the dining room is a slightly raised platform from the floor upon which a group of six people are playing dinner music. There is a piano player, two violin players, two viola players and a bass player all making beautiful soft dinner music. With soft lights and soft music your mind is truly set free to wander in any direction it may choose. The atmosphere is one of complete relaxation as time endlessly flows by. Further, to make any woman feel very special, each lady entering the restaurant is handed a beautiful red rose by papa, the owner of the establishment. What a gracious way to make a lady feel very special.

Now after a wonderful meal and I might add a relaxing one, I guess I should get my check, pay my bill, and head back to the hotel. However, in this relaxed mood I'm in, I don't have the urge to get up and leave just yet. They have just completed playing *The Count of Luxembourg Waltz* and did an excellent rendition I may add. Their next selection sounds like *The Gypsy Princess Waltz*. Yep, I'm not wrong. I know that I should go, but I'll stay a little longer and try to absorb as much as I can as I'm sure in Erzurum good music is too far removed. However, I'm told that they do get the *Voice Of America* from Rhodes via short wave radio in Erzurum. If that is the case, it is something to look forward to during the long cold winter nights.

Morning has rolled around rather quickly or it was a shorter night than usual. Be that as it may, I had better get my bags together and get them downstairs just in case Sergeant Morris should arrive on time. I dislike people who are not punctual and usually end up telling them so. Me and my big mouth. One day I'll end up putting my foot into it.

'Hi Sergeant Crocker, all ready I see.'

'That's correct and I see that you are on time for a change.'

'That's hitting a little below the belt wouldn't you say?'

'Not really when you are on the receiving end, wouldn't you say?'

'Point taken. By the way, I stopped by the Message Centre and picked up your distribution for the team.'

'Thanks very much, I appreciate it.'

'When we get to the train station the baggage handlers will take all the items you had stored in the Field Training Store Room and place them in the baggage car for you. They will then place all your personal baggage in your sleeping car. After that, you will pay them for their services.'

'Just how much should I pay them?'

'With what you have I guess 150.00 Turkish Lira will well cover your cost. Here comes the train, and it is right on time. I was told that this train is one leg of the old Orient Express which has its origin in Paris. Beats the hell out of me, I don't know where it get's it's origin.'

'You know Sergeant Morris, you would make a fantastic tourist guide if you had any facts or figures to play around with.'

'I have plenty of figures.'

'I'm sure you do, but we had better drop the subject matter there.'

'This is your car here. Get on, put your things in your compartment, and I'll wait here. Now that's better with the window open, so we can talk.'

'You were saying that you plan on leaving Ankara soon.'

'If all goes well in about three months I'll be heading back home. Oh oh, we are starting to move.'

'By the way, when do I know when to get off this train? What was that? When I run out of track? When is that?'

'You'll find out.'

'Damn it to hell, that's no answer. He can't hear me and I can't hear him. I knew he was a smart ass bastard the first time I met him. Look at him, just standing there laughing at me.' I guess he has had his jollies for the day. If it's a joke, it's sick.

As the train is slowly pulling out of the Ankara train station, new apprehensions seem to creep into my mind. My God, I'm on train and to the best of my knowledge not another person that I have heard speaks English or even pidgin English. Further, I haven't ascertained just how many days or nights it will take me to get to Erzurum. What a hell of a way to undertake a trip. You know you are on your way, but you don't know where in the hell you're going to end up. What a smart ass he turned out to be. Ah, it takes all kinds.

My compartment is very nice and looks like pictures that I had seen in the movies of the Orient Express. As you look around the compartment you can see the very fancy inlaid wood work done on the walls. The little lights in the compartment only add to the beauty and the comfort for the passenger. However, my one main question is answered when I place my hand on the covered heater in the car. To be sure, it is nice and hot and all is very comfortable. While getting my things sorted out and hanging up my overcoat there is a knock on the compartment door. In my best high school French, I told whoever it was at the door to enter. That was stupidity on my part as it could have been anyone. As it turned out it was my porter who would be taking care of me during my trip. As soon as he entered, he started speaking to me in French and stopped only when he didn't receive any reply. I looked at him and he looked at me. He spoke Turkish and French. I spoke English, Japanese, German, Spanish and a little Hebrew. Except for sign language and drawing it seems we have a slight communication problem. Being a professional porter, he could sense straight away that I was a phoney baloney when it came to speaking French. I can see that this is going to be a real fun trip. Who am I kidding? However, I do believe that I did get something out of the conversation. He held up three fingers and made a motion like eating. This indicated like I was being given a 3rd sitting and not first or second sitting for my meals. In short, I could take my time and not feel rushed and perchance maybe learn a few words in Turkish. Well, that's hopeful or wishful thinking on my part and I'll let the chips fall where they may. However, there is one thing I know for certain and that is there is no *Bomb Sight* toilet in my compartment. No, it's a regular Western style toilet that folds up when the door is closed. Can you picture me trying to do a balancing act on a moving train? I wonder what the poor people do in the Economy Class? I sure feel for them.

Sitting here looking out the window and watching the countryside whiz by with its beautiful clean coat of white snow glistening through the clouds when the sunrays breaks forth. It's a picture to behold which any artist would be most happy to paint. There goes the *ding dong* for the first meal sitting. Come to think of it, I'm sneaking up on the hungry side. What was that? It sounded like the porter dropped his *ding dong* as we went round that last curve. I can tell ya it sure made one hell of a noise. Hope the porter is okay. From the sound of it, his one note on his *ding dong* is a little on the flat side. We must be coming into some sort of a city as there are more houses, people and paved streets. That sign looked like it read Kirşehir, so it must be the next city or town. We are slowing down, so we must be stopping to pick up someone or to let someone off. As we pull into the station, there are a number of children selling many and varied items. The best customers must be the people in the Economy Class who do not use the dining car. There are all types of breads, fruit, candies, and even home made sweaters spun out of wool. As we pull out of the station the children and some of the older people wave to us and have smiles on their faces.

From the sound of the *ding dong*, I would say that they had gotten it repaired. It does sound a wee bit better than it did after the fall. That is the second sitting. When these people complete feeding their faces, it will be my time to put on the feed bag. The way my stomach is grumbling the Third Sitting can't come too soon. It looks like we are starting to climb as more mountains are becoming apparent with each black puff of smoke. Yes, yes, there goes the *ding dong* for the third sitting.

As I leave my compartment I lock the door and advance towards the dining car with great anticipation of that which I know I'm about to receive. God, am I hungry. As I enter the dining car, I'm given a number which will be my table for the duration of the trip. The dining car is everything I had expected it to be. Brass lamps on the table, silver salt and pepper shakers, crisp white table cloths, sparkling glass ware, with bottled water. The setting of silverware was in it's proper place and all shining with no finger marks on it. Further, I can see that the setting on the table is for one. Folded beside the silverware is a crisp dinner napkin which could cover my lap and the person next to me should there be one. In short, I'm very impressed with what I have seen thus far and I haven't even seen the meal yet. I can hear the Turkish couple just across from me order something that sounds like *cobra* I have heard that rattlesnake is tasty, but I heard nothing about *cobra*. I don't know what it is, but I'll write it down as it sounded. In a jiffy the waiter returns with two steaming hot bowls of whatever it was. He serves them and then turns to me. Since I don't have a clue to what he is saying, he says *cobra*? I nodded yes, as if I really knew what he was offering me. I say to myself, it can't be too bad as the people across the aisle from me seem to be enjoying the hell out of what they are eating. He brings me my *cobra* and it looks good. With my sign language I motion for him to write it down as I'm pointing to my *cobra* . Okay, so I had to ask him five times to write it down before he got the message. I guess my sign language is a little rusty from my three years in Japan. He writes *cobra*. I see that under the C he has placed a (,). It looks like this Ç. Later I find out that Ç takes on the CH sound. To get the correct sound in English you would have to spell it like *Chorba*. In short, soup. He now brings me some beautiful Turkish bread. Again I ask him what it is in Turkish and he spells it for me. *Ekmek*. I'm sure making fast progress as I already know two words in Turkish, soup and bread. I now look at my soup and wonder what is in it. I can see some finely chopped carrots, potatoes, leeks, tomatoes and something white which looks like meat. The more that I look at the white stuff the more I recall in my high school biology class that it looked a good deal like brains. However, these were cut up and much smaller and would fit into a category the size of a sheep. By the time that I had unravelled this mystery, I had eaten most of my vegetables and most of the broth. Thank God I hadn't eaten any of that white stuff as they were lamb's brains. That's what the waiter told me. I'm sure that they were good, but I sure in hell didn't fancy some. I pushed the soup away and the waiter smiled, looked at me and took my soup away. He got the message. We are sure getting better with our sign language. Lamb's brains, yuk! The main course consisted of a nice tender fillet of beef with golden brown potato wedges and green beans. A fresh green salad with lettuce, shredded carrots, green onions, and tomatoes was also popped on the table. The salad dressing was vinegar and olive oil. With such a meal placed before me I took my time and enjoyed each mouthful. I took more time than usual and waited until most people had departed the dining car so I could add a few more Turkish words to my vocabulary. I did learn to say water *(su)*, milk *(sut)*, bread *(ekmek)*, soup *(çorba)*, onion *(sogan)* and a couple of more words. Now that's not too bad. When you think of it, when I got on this train I didn't know one word of Turkish.

With that very delightful meal over with, except for the lamb's brains soup, I retired to my compartment for a well earned rest. With the clickety clack of the wheels over the rails I soon found myself fast asleep and enjoying every minute of it. Later when I awoke I could see that the landscape had changed and there were many more trees and a few streams popping up now and then. By the time we got to Kayseri we were well on our way into the high country. More and more mountains seem to be coming into the picture all the time. Beautiful mountains with more and more trees all decked with its wintry white coat of crystal snow were now passing in review. The many villages we passed people would come out and wave at the train all bundled up to keep the bitter winter from engulfing them. If this is cold now, I thought, just how cold is it going to be when I arrive in Erzurum. Perish the thought I said to myself, as I pulled closer to the heater in my nice warm compartment. Later, the porter came in and made up my bed for the night. Of course I have visions of a rather hard mattress and a sleepless night, but that would be normal under the circumstances on a train. Would you believe, nothing could be further from the truth. The bed was just excellent and most comfortable. Knowing me, I gave it a try prior to putting the bed to use for the night. When I got tired of watching the countryside pass by and looking for lights in the night, I then decided that a few winks would be in order. I must have been more tired than I realised as I didn't hear another thing until the porter knocked on my door. I unlocked the door and would you believe there was a nice steaming hot cup of tea being offered to me. He departed with a smile leaving me to enjoy what he had brought me. He returned later inquiring if I would like another cup. Knowing that breakfast was just a *ding dong* away, I thanked him kindly but said no. With that out of the way, he started to put my compartment in order once again. He took off the old sheets and replaced them with freshly starched sheets and pillow cases. In no time at all my compartment was in a number one shape with everything cleaned and dusted. It was like, now you see him, now you don't. Before long I heard the *ding dong* and knew it was time for me to get my butt in gear and get to the dining car. As I'm seated, I'm wondering just what type of Turkish food is going to be the offering for breakfast. Oh yes, I didn't forget my pen and pad. Pray tell, how else am I going to get my Turkish lesson without any pain or strain? A very nice Turkish breakfast was suggested so I accepted. Frankly I cheated. I just looked across and saw what the people across the aisle were having so I just pointed to the waiter and nodded my head. It consisted of white goat's cheese *(beyaz peynir)*, hard boiled eggs *(kati yumurta)*, Turkish bread toasted *(kizarmis Ekmek)*, butter *(tere-yağ)* with assorted jams *(reçel)* and plenty of hot tea *(çay)*. Having never tasted anything like that before, I could say it was fit for a king. In short, it was just damn good. Needless to say, by the time I reach this place they call Erzurum, I'll be a first class interpreter. I say again. When I got on board this Iron Horse I couldn't even say 'Thank you'. However, one main problem still remains. That is, when in hell do we get to this place they call Erzurum? As best as I can tell, we haven't run out of track as of yet.

More towns, cities and villages have come and gone with strange sounding names like; Akdagmadeni, Sivas, and heading for a city called Erzincan. In addition to all of this, we have been playing hide and seek with a river called the Euphrates and its tributaries. Beautiful cascading water comes tumbling down the mountain side which are surrounded by tall green pine trees on either side of it's banks. When I was first told that I was going to Turkey, I had a picture in my mind of sand and more sand. However, nothing could be further from the truth. These beautiful pine trees as a backdrop, are facts and not distorted pictures of my mind. One would have to see this beauty first hand to believe it and appreciate it. Between thee and me I would say that this is one of Turkey's best kept secrets. Who in their right mind would want a lot of tourists running around messing up this beautiful country. Not me.

We have stopped in this little village for some reason, but I know not why. Looking out my window, just across the opening, is a small house with a gentle smoke coming forth out of the chimney which curls around the trees like a dance of the seven veils. Our stop is very brief and once again we are on our way. Miles and miles have passed and we still haven't run out of track. We seem to be getting closer to the city called Erzincan and should reach it by night fall. After that I'm told the next big city is Erzurum. If that be true, that would give us two nights and two days on this train. Yes, the porter in his best sign language told me that we should reach Erzurum just after lunch or around 2.30 pm tomorrow. I can say that I have really enjoyed this trip, but frankly I'm getting rather tired of living out of a duffel bag. Here it is now January and I've been on the go since November from New Mexico, to California, to New Jersey, back to California, back to New Jersey, across the Atlantic Ocean to England, then on to Germany, where I spent three days including Christmas, then on to Istanbul, Turkey, with one night stand there prior to leaving for Ankara the following day. After arriving in Ankara with no sponsor to meet me, no Turkish lira to meet my expenses, no common language to communicate with people, cold, miserable, hungry, and in general, just depressed. Looking on the bright side, the best I can hope for is that something good will come out of all of this.

I've had my lunch and have my bags and all of my belongings together just waiting to run out of train track. In the distance against the shining backdrop of snow covered hills, would appear to be a town or a city. It's hard to tell from this angle. Could this be my fabled city of Erzurum? I hate to admit it, but I'm beginning to get a little excited about this adventure as well as a little apprehensive around the edges. It shouldn't be too much longer before we reach the outskirts of the city. With the wind blowing and the black smoke billowing before us acting like a vanguard heralding our triumphal entry into this ancient city of Erzurum. As we draw nearer to the train station, it would appear that half of the population of this city have come to greet us.

Looking out of my compartment window at this angle, I can see the high barriers which would indicate that this is the end of the line . . . no more track.

By this time, there must be at least four hundred people here looking for an advantage point. Jokingly I say to myself, 'Here I am people' come and greet me. Some people wave at me and I wave back. Now I'm beginning to wonder just who the important VIP is on the train. My porter came to my compartment and took my bag off of the train. In return I tipped him very well and he was most graceful and happy. After all, it was he who made my trip bearable. Oh yes, I also left a good tip for my Turkish teacher, the waiter.

Standing there in my uniform with my name tag in full view, a man came up to me and wanted to know if I was Sergeant Crocker. I smiled at him and said, 'and just whom were you expecting, Genghis Khan?' He broke out laughing and acknowledged that his question was after all rather foolish since my name tag was in full view.

'Did you have a good trip?' he inquired.

'Not too bad considering not knowing any Turkish made the trip a little awkward and a little stressful at times. Other than that it was a very beautiful trip. By the way, what are all these people waiting for?'

'Oh, nothing special. Whenever the train comes into Erzurum many of the townspeople who can get away from their homes come down to see who is coming into town, meet their friends, and get caught up on the latest gossip. Don't worry, you'll make the local gossip rounds in every Çay Evi (Tea House) by night fall and by tomorrow, they will know your name and most of your family's history. Do you have the slips for the baggage you shipped from Ankara?'

'Yes, right here.'

'You wait here and I'll get the baggage and the truck and then we'll be off to the hotel. Sergeant Crocker please excuse my manners, for not introducing myself. I'm 1st Lieutenant Morgan, the Administrative Officer of the Team. You'll be my right hand man, so to speak, in the Administration Department. We have a Sergeant Bilman, but he is junior to you in rank, so you'll be second in charge of Administration.'

'Lt. Morgan out here in the frozen mountains, miles from nowhere, who really gives a darn about rank. I would think that the most important thing is to get our mission accomplished to the best of our ability.'

'It's great to think that way Sergeant Crocker, but you haven't been introduced to our Team Chief, Colonel Jordan.

'What you are saying Lt Morgan, I'm in for a rude awakening?'

'Something like that.'

'Lt. Morgan, the one thing that I have learned in my short life thus far, is that everything in life can be reduced to a common denominator. Case in point which comes to mind is that of David over Goliath. A sling and a stone was the common denominator.'

'Let me put it another way Sergeant Crocker, no one on the Team has found that common denominator so far as it pertains to Colonel Jordan. He has made people's lives here a living hell and even some of our Turkish counterparts.'

'Like I said Lt. Morgan, there has to be a common denominator lurking somewhere just waiting to jump out when he least expects it and when he is most vulnerable.'

'Well, this is the Güvenal Palas, which will be your home for the next twelve months. I'll have our Turkish soldiers that live here help you get your things up to your room.'

'Thank you very much.' At this point a young Turkish boy, who was a soldier, but did not wear his uniform came up to me and said, 'Welcome Sergeant Crocker, to FTT 3-A.'

'Thank you,' I said.'

'My name is Yilmaz and I'm here to help you.' His English was excellent. Another thing, he had blonde hair and very blue eyes, oh yes, and a very nice smile. When my baggage was placed in my room, Yilmaz did a vanishing act seemingly right before my very eyes. Later I found him in the kitchen getting the Team's evening meal prepared. Yilmaz, I found out later was our cook, interpreter, hotel manager, and just about anything else you could think of that required attention. He was our jack of all trades. Prior to the evening meal, Lt. Morgan came by to tell me that we dressed for dinner here. I laughed and said, 'Lt. Morgan, did you think that I was coming to dinner nude.'

'No Sergeant Crocker, I meant that Colonel Jordan has a rule that we all wear coat and tie for the evening meal.'

'Lt. Morgan, you must be joking, out here in the middle of nowhere.'

'That's right.'

'Thanks for informing me.' When the dinner bell rang forth, everyone moved out of their room and into the dining room. To be sure, you were seated by rank and being a Non-Commissioned Officer (NCO) I was seated at the far end of the table. Just one more seat, and I would have been out the front door, that's how far down I was. Next to me sat Sergeant Bilman. While the food was being placed on the table, Colonel Jordan tapped on his water glass and made the following announcement. 'Gentlemen, as you can see, we have a new team member, Sergeant Crocker.' Looking at me he said, 'Sergeant' he said sarcastically, 'you sure took your sweet time getting your ass out here.' You could hear the others' eye balls click. I stood up, looking him right in the eye and said, 'you are very correct Colonel Jordan, however, I only stopped long enough to bury my mother who just recently passed away.' With that remark, I walked out of the dining room without asking if I could be excused. You could hear a pin drop. No one, but no one ever spoke to Colonel Jordan like that and lived to tell about it. Well I did, and I just think that he has found his common denominator. At the time, I didn't know it, but Yilmaz was standing just outside the dining room and saw that I had walked out and heard what I had said to Colonel Jordan. When the evening meal was over, he came to my room and brought me several sandwiches and a

54

cup of coffee. As he put the tray down he looked at me and said, 'Sergeant Crocker, I'm very sorry for what the Colonel said to you this evening, it wasn't very nice of him to say that.'

'Thank you Yilmaz, it was very kind of you to come and to bring me this tray.'

'Thank you very much.' Under normal circumstances there is a movie shown in the dining room every night after the evening meal, but somehow, the movie wasn't shown tonight. Further, Colonel Jordan didn't venture out of his room that night.

The following morning I was up early ready to face the day and to get a look at my new office in the Third Turkish Army Headquarters. While I was sitting at the table finishing my breakfast with one of the other officers, Colonel Jordan came out with a rather long face, looked at me and didn't say anything. To show that I wasn't angry with him I said, 'Good Morning Colonel.' He turned around, looked at me, and snapped. 'Just what's the fucking good about it?' I smiled at him and answered, 'Well sir, that is your question, and I would suggest that if you want an answer, you answer it.' With that, I got up from the table and went back to my room. I got my coat and asked Yilmaz for the directions to the Third Turkish Army Headquarters and left. Needless to say it didn't take very long for that encounter to get around to the team members. Privately, they were all saying, 'go boy go.' However, even being in the military, I just couldn't see why these men were taking all this crap Colonel Jordan was dishing out to them. To me, the answer should have been obvious. After I had been in my job for about a month as the Administrative NCO I by chance stumbled across the Colonel's trump card. Three quarters of the Team's Officers would leave before Colonel Jordan would which would make Colonel Jordan their Rating Officer on their Efficiency Reports. So what you may ask? In this case, Colonel Jordan as the Rating Officer, holds sway over their entire military career. A bad Efficiency Report will affect that officer's future assignments, future promotions, and just about everything that officer does in his military career. In short, it's a death sentence, period. If it's a good report, so be it. However, if it is a bad report or a low report, the officer concerned had better make plans to get out of the service. In short, he is a marked man. In my case, Colonel Jordan is not my Rating Officer only my Endorsing Officer, but he will be long gone when I'm due for my Efficiency Rating. My last Efficiency Rating was accomplished by my Commanding Officer at White Sands Proving

Grounds. I can add, that it was a damn good rating even if I do say so myself. I somehow feel that General Hall had a hand in it somewhere. However, I shall never know.

During that day I had spoken to several interpreters and asked them in what hotel they were living. They pointed out that they were in the Europa Otel just across the square from the Güvenal Palas. I asked one of the interpreters Mumtaz, if it would be possible for me to come to their hotel and just listen to them speak Turkish?

'I can't see any problem,' he said, 'so come and join us after your evening meal.' At the office were two dictionaries. One was English to Turkish and the other was Turkish to English. In any event, I could hear and learn sounds and then later words. After a short while I was beginning to start to carry a short conversation, small as it was in Turkish. I felt that I was beginning to make a little progress and felt very good about it. However, when Colonel Jordan learned of my Turkish classes, he let it be known that I wasn't to be going to the interpreter's hotel regardless for any reason. What a narrow minded bastard. Of course, he has made no effort to learn any Turkish whatsoever and has become very suspicious of anyone who does. I think it would be safe to say that he is becoming paranoid. In short, I was beginning to come to grips with the Turkish language. What really would burn the Colonel's ass was when some of the Turkish officers here in the headquarters would speak to me and I would answer them in Turkish. Needless to say what hit the fan. Frankly, I couldn't care less, as I viewed him as a large piece of cow dung heading for the crap pile. I will of course be a little more discreet and let him see less of me doing the things that I thought would improve my knowledge and education of Turkey. After all, I was only a guest in their country and should act accordingly.

Sunday morning rolled around and I was cold during the night as the weather dropped a few more degrees. I went into the kitchen to where Yilmaz was and asked him if we had any more blankets here in the hotel. No, Sergeant Crocker, but after breakfast I can take you to the Government Store to see if they have any blankets for sale.'

'That will be great. When can we depart here?'

'I have twenty minutes of work to complete before I can leave.'

'Okay, I'll be in my room when you are ready.'

As we depart the Güvenal Palas, we turn right and not left as we usually do. 'Where are we going Yilmaz?'

'Sir, I thought that I would show you a little bit of Erzurum which most Americans never see. This way, you'll be able to see the stalls where the vendors sell their goods, fruits and vegetables to the people of the city.'

'That sounds very interesting.' As we move into the general area, I can see many more stands loaded with fruit and vegetables. As we approach one of the stalls, the man is very busy putting out some large and beautiful peaches for sale. When we got closer, I pointed my finger in the direction of the man's stall and said to Yilmaz, 'look at these beautiful peaches.'

'Peaches! Peaches!' was the loud cry from the man behind the stall counter as he dashed out whirling a large knife.

'Yilmaz, Yilmaz, what in the hell is wrong with that man?' I shouted.

Yilmaz was laughing, but this man was getting closer and I didn't find this situation too healthy or to be a laughing situation. 'Stop, stop.' Yilmaz yelled in Turkish. Thank God the man stopped. 'Did you hear what that American said to me,' the stall keeper screamed at Yilmaz? By this time Yilmaz had stopped laughing and had gotten serious. 'That American didn't say anything to you.' Pointing at me. 'He was only saying what beautiful seftali you had. 'No, no, he said peach.'

'No, no,' Yilmaz continued. 'In English şeftali means peach, and peach in Turkish means,'

'No, no, peach in Turkish means bastard . . . and he called me a bastard.' After a very hot discussion for about ten to twelve minutes the man finally concluded that I really didn't mean any harm and it was only a misunderstanding in languages. I think that I had messed my pants when he came at me with the knife, as I was sure that I was going to be done in. Thank you, that is much too close to me for comfort. I made up my mind for the time being that I would keep my mouth shut while I was out in public. As we were leaving the area, the man behind the stall counter came forth and gave me four of his largest şeftali and called me Abi. I thanked him, but I didn't ask what abi meant until I had departed that area. I finally asked Yilmaz what Abi meant. 'It means brother,' he said with a big smile.

'Yea, thirty minutes ago I was about to have my throat cut from ear to ear, and now he calls me brother. I can understand that events can change fast in this changing world, but this is much too fast to suit me.

As we start off in another direction I'm beginning to get a feeling of relief just to be out of that general area. We finally reach the main street and it starts to snow again. Just a few doors down the street we come upon the Government Store. I have to show my Red Book, issued from the Turkish General Staff in Ankara, before I'm permitted into the store. Yes, they had two pure wool blankets, but again I must produce my Red Book once again. The blankets were for a double bed, but I only had a single bed, but I could care less just so they kept me warm during the cold winter nights. What I didn't know until later, that after the evening meal when the winter ration of coal was in short supply, most team members went to their room and went to bed just to keep warm. This will give you some idea just how cold it gets out in Eastern Turkey.

While we were walking down the main street, little kids were using garbage lids as sleds and were having a ball sliding down the slight hill. 'Yilmaz,' I asked, 'what is that round building over to the left? Yes, that one.'

'It's the building where they placed the people who died during the winter.'

'What do they do with them after they placed them there?'

'Nothing, they just wait there until the ground is not frozen. When it is not frozen they take them out of there and bury them. During the winter they cannot even break the ground as it is frozen solid. They just tag them and bury them when they can.' That sure answered my question.

As the days and months passed, there was to be a very large military exercise which would require all of the team members to be gone for two weeks into the field with their counterparts. Lt Morgan came to me and wanted to know if I wanted to go to Ankara to do the Courier Run, as Sgt Bilman had just gotten back from Ankara. He explained, that with the team gone, he would have to remain at the office during the departure of all the other officers. It was settled, that I would go to Ankara, do the team's shopping plus any of my own. Prior to their departure, I'll go around and ask them if there is anything special any of the officers want from Ankara while I'm there. I hope the good Colonel doesn't think that I'm going soft and want to get on the good side of him. That's the last impression I would want to give him. Further, I'll check with the Post Exchange Officer to see if he wants me to get anything special for our two wall locker PX. Frankly, it would be very laughable if it wasn't on the serious side. From what I can gather, that is the way 'Big Daddy', (Colonel Jordan), wants it.

What Big Daddy wants Big Daddy gets. So much for the PX Wall Locker.

'Well gentlemen, while you are gone, be careful and I'll do the same. I have all your lists and even the list that Lt Morgan gave me for Colonel Jordan.'

'You mean that he didn't give you his list, but gave it to Lt Morgan.'

'You've got that correct. Something is most wrong somewhere, but I'll just let it go at that.'

'I suppose all of you are coming down to the train to see me off like all of the rest of the town folks?'

'Wouldn't miss it for the world.'

'By the way, just what time does the train depart Erzurum?'

'If it departs on time, it will be around 1600 hours.'

'OK, I'll see you at the train.'

From the looks of it, most of the townspeople are here to wave bye bye to the train. For the most part, it seems a bit warmer today but the ground is still very frozen which means that the snow cover will remain for a long time to come. I'm sure one day I'll see some green grass and the trees blooming as it can't remain cold all the time. 'I'm over here.' As I look out the window of the train, I can see that most of the team members are here at the station all except you know who. Remember men, should you require anything while I'm in Ankara, just be sure you send your request by courier pigeon as you sure in hell won't make it by telephone.'

'See ya.' With these words of wisdom, a big black puff of smoke rolled forth from the train's stack and I'm on my way to Ankara.

The trip to Ankara was beautiful and most enjoyable. Sitting in my compartment I saw the rushing and dashing streams sparkling like diamonds as they tumbled ever downwards to join their mother, the Euphrates River. However, the trip back to Ankara was by far more enjoyable as I knew many more phrases in Turkish and could communicate with people. I wasn't isolated and was much more freer and relaxed. One thing for sure, I didn't have to worry as to when I was going to run out of train track and all that crap. On Friday morning I went into the JAMMAT Army Section Administrative Office and took my documents and distribution and got rid of them. After that, I went to the snack bar downstairs to get myself a good cup of coffee and a donut. While I was there I met Joyce Backhouse who was also in early and came down for a cup of coffee. Seeing me, she asked if I'd mind if she joined me. I was most happy to have her company and indicated same. 'You're in early on your first Courier Trip aren't you?'

'Yes,' I answered.

'That's right,' she continued, 'the team in Erzurum is out in the field for the next two weeks.' I thought to myself, boy she is a pretty smart cookie and has the answers. I like that.

'By the way,' I asked, 'where do they hold church services here in Ankara?'

'Right here in JAMMAT auditorium. If you should come, I may just see you here.'

I've gone to the Commissary Store, and have that taken care of, gone to the Class VI Store, and made all of their purchases, which leaves me only the Post Exchange. I haven't done too badly. I only have to get everything to the FTT-3A store room and get it packed for the trip back to Erzurum. Knowing the ropes, I haven't wasted any time getting all of the business taken care of. This leaves me a lot of free time to do some of the things that I want to do for myself. I head back to the Buliver Palas and have a nice long bath and relax. I planned on going out to dinner tonight, but my relaxing period lasted until 9.45 p.m. I just went downstairs and had a cheese sandwich in the Bulivar Palas Restaurant and called it a night.

Sunday morning I was up early, went downstairs into the Buliver Palas Restaurant and had a very good continental type breakfast. Since the hotel was located only four blocks from JAMMAT, I thought I would go to church. As an extra incentive, maybe Mrs Backhouse would be there and I would know someone. When I arrived the Base Chaplain seemed to be in some sort of a tizzy and didn't seem too well pleased. I asked him if something was wrong and if I could help him. He was abrupt and said something like his soloist couldn't make it and he had built his sermon around the solo. People had started to arrive as the organist was playing. 'Excuse me Chaplain, but what was your soloist going to sing?' I asked. With the flip of his hand he said, 'the Holy City.' Looking at him I asked, 'what key is it in Chaplain?' He was so upset he almost gave me a rude answer. He checked with the organist and came back and said it was in B Flat. 'Good,' I said, 'I can help you in your hour of need if you still want it sung.' For a split second, I thought I was going to have an in body experience right there before God and everybody as the Chaplain suddenly grabbed me, hugged me to express his feelings and his gratitude. Mrs Backhouse had arrived with some of her friends and were seated near the back of the auditorium. They all looked very pretty in their Sunday best. However, I was in my military uniform. As the church service progressed, the Chaplain announced the special soloist this morning would be Sergeant Crocker from JAMMAT. I stood up, nodded to the organist, and we started. I didn't know how well she played nor she know how well I sang, but we started. When we got into the song, she grew in confidence as well as myself. To hear us perform one would be led to believe that we did this every Sunday. I looked at the Chaplain, and he was praying I think. When the solo was completed, the Chaplain just looked to heaven and I think he said, 'Thank you.' While I was singing, I had noticed a man seated in the middle of the congregation wearing a reddish brown suit who kept looking at me like he knew me. After several side glances, I knew that I didn't know him so I paid no more attention to him. Mrs Backhouse seemed pleased with my solo as did her friends. In all, the Chaplain's sermon wasn't too bad which dealt with the rejoicing and the triumphal entrance into Jerusalem of Jesus riding on the back of an ass. As the last Amen was played and sung, the Chaplain indicated that refreshments were being served just outside in the hallway and all were invited to partake. The Chaplain thanked me again and wanted to know if I would be available the following Sunday.

'No Chaplain,' I said, 'I'm stationed out near the Russian border and it would be most difficult travelling back and forth.'

Mrs Backhouse called me over to meet her good friends Bob and Dot Gordon.

We were introduced and they seemed a very lovely couple. I also mentioned to Mrs Backhouse that Mrs Gordon could well pass for her sister. They laughed, as that had been said before. We then proceeded with our coffee. While we were talking, the man in the reddish brown suit came up to us and said that he enjoyed my rendition of *The Holy City*. I said, 'Thank you Sir,' and then turned my back to him. 'Excuse me Sergeant,' he said a few minutes later, 'I see you are wearing the 9th Army shoulder patch?'

'Yes Sir.'

'I was in the 9th US Army overseas,' he related to me.

'That's nice sir,' I said with a smile, and promptly turned my back to him once more. I returned to my conversation with Mrs Backhouse and Mr and Mrs Gordon. Damn it, this man interrupted our conversation once again.

'Are you stationed here in Ankara?' he asked.

'No sir, I'm stationed in Erzurum.' Once again, I turn my back on him. I've noticed that during my conversation with this man, neither Mrs Backhouse or the Gordons enter into the conversation. I can only assume that he must be some kind of a crack pot and they don't want to get involved with him. Once again I turned my back on him and resumed my conversation. 'Do they always have as many people attending.' Before I can complete my sentence, this man interrupted me once again.

'Sergeant,' he says, 'in two weeks, time I'm coming out to Erzurum.' Again I looked at him and said, 'Sir, that's nice,' and again, I turned my back on him. You would think by this time, that he would get the message that I didn't care to speak to him. All this time, Mrs Backhouse was watching the proceedings but still didn't enter into the conversation. Frankly, I didn't blame her, as this old fart could drive anyone around the bend. I placed my cup on the table and made some remark like, with this old man always interrupting our conversation, maybe we can all meet later for a light lunch and continue our conversation. I'm more than sure that this man heard my remark but he only looked. As we started to leave the man asked me how things were at the Field Training Team 3-A?

'Well sir, I believe we could all learn the fuller meaning of the word tranquillity.'

'Just a minute Sergeant, allow me to introduce myself.'

'Yes Sir.'

'I'm Major General Reed, and I command all the troops under the jurisdiction JAMMAT here in Turkey.'

'Yes Sir.'

'Tomorrow morning, I want you in my office at 0900 hours sharp.'

'Yes Sir,' Oh shit, I thought to myself, now what have I done to deserve something like this? I really wasn't very nice to him, but by the same token I wasn't rude and always said, 'Yes Sir.' Now I can fully understand why Mrs Backhouse didn't take an active part in our conversation, as it was her boss, the General. After that encounter, I really didn't feel too much like going any place and excused myself. I went back to my hotel and started to review my conversation with the General. My Sunday was ruined with the words, 'I'll see you in my office at 0900 sharp tomorrow.'

That damn business with the General worried me all night as he could say, come in Sergeant, sit down Private and that would be the end of my military career.

Since I have plenty of time I'll get myself all dolled up in my Sunday going to meeting uniform and try to make a good impression on the General. Later, I'll have a cup of tea strong, and a slice of toast. Frankly, I don't feel much like eating at present. If I was a drinking man I probably would have gone out and gotten myself good and drunk, and would only have made the situation even worse. At least I don't have a hangover to contend with. Since it is about 8.15 am I'll do a slow walk to JAMMAT Headquarters and hope that the general has changed his mind about seeing me. As I enter the general's office at 8.45 am Mrs Backhouse is busy as usual, but stops to bid me a bright and happy good morning. 'How is the old man this morning?' I ask.

'He seemed bright and happy when he came in this morning. Come to think of it,' she continued, 'you don't look too bright and happy.'

'Would you be if you didn't know what fate was hanging over your head. I heard tell that they call him the *Red snapper!*'

'True, but I don't think he'll be snapping at you in this case.'

'How can you be so sure?'

'I can't be, but he doesn't seem to be in a snapping mood. Between you and me, I think he is searching for information about your Team Chief.' It's now one minute to nine and I'll go in and inform the general that you are here.'

'Don't hurry just on my account.' Mrs Backhouse goes into the general's office and she is right out once again. 'The General will see you Sergeant Crocker.' She holds the door open as I make my grand entrance into the chamber of doom. I'm now standing on a red carpet which leads to the general's desk about fifteen yards from the door. As I enter I walk towards the desk and stop about ten feet from the desk and report. 'Sergeant Crocker reporting as ordered Sir.' He returns my salute and said, 'Come in Sergeant, and have a chair over here.' Oh my God, he said have a chair Sergeant. 'Firstly, I want to thank you again for filling in for the soloist at the eleventh hour. The Chaplain told me you didn't even have a warm up with the organist but went into it cold. I call that having real guts.'

'Well General Reed, the Chaplain had a rather serious problem and I felt if I had it in my power to alleviate the situation, I should do so.'

'I like that attitude in my young soldiers. Just keep up the good work.'

'Now this brings us to the business as to why I called you to my office this morning. I checked with Mrs Backhouse this morning and she informed me that I'll be going to Erzurum in three weeks and not in two weeks as I told you yesterday. I was most interested in what you had to say about learning a better meaning of the word tranquillity. Now just what did you mean with that remark? Now don't be afraid to express yourself fully, as others from the team have done so in the past.'

'Sir, it's like this. I was nearly a month late getting to my assignment in Erzurum due to the fact that my mother had passed away just prior to my departure from the States. I had to fly from the East Coast to the West Coast to see that she was laid to rest. My first night in Erzurum, Colonel Jordan introduced me but then added that I sure in hell took my time getting here. It was very sarcastically stated and made to look like the entire situation was my fault.' At this point the General took out pencil and paper and started to make some notes. 'I'll apologise for him Sergeant, as that was a very cruel and crude thing for him to say.'

'Further General, the language he uses at all of us is very unreal.'

'I've got the message Sergeant. Do you have a PX facility there?'

'We have Sir, if you call two wall lockers nearly empty most of the time a PX.' After a few more questions he looks at his watch and tells me that he must leave the headquarters and go to the Turkish General Staff for a meeting. 'Sergeant Crocker, you have been very helpful and I appreciate your time this morning.'

'Thank you General,' as I stand up and salute, make a smart about face and depart his office. Come to think of it, have you ever sat at attention for forty minutes with your heart in your mouth? I did.

When I returned to the Army Administrative Section, the personnel there were betting that I may return as a Private after my visit with the general.

'No such luck men.'

'What did you talk about?'

'Frankly, it doesn't happen to be any of your business.'

'Aren't you going to give us a little hint?'

'Not even.' I think I've had enough of these city people for one day. They give me the shits. The one thing I did get out of the general's meeting is that he is not taking the train out to Erzurum, but will fly out in one of the C-54s. I can only say he will be missing a very beautiful trip, but then again I guess he has more important things to do than watch the countryside go by.

The trip back to Erzurum was very beautiful with the Spring thaw sending additional water rushing towards the mighty Euphrates southwards to nourish the peoples of Syria and Iraq. Yes, you can sit here and let your mind wander and conjure up all sorts of images both bad and good. What would happen to the peoples of Syria and Iraq if suddenly the water supply was cut to just a fine trickle or stopped altogether. How many millions of people would die not to mention all other forms of life which are supported by these waters? That thought sure sets the mind boggling. Now that I have given myself a good scare I had better start thinking of more happier things. We are only a few hours out of Erzurum and I'm wondering if my good Colonel Jordan has cleaned up his act? However, I'm not telling him or anyone about my trip to General Reed's office..or what was discussed. I too can have a few things up my sleeve like some of the others. This is called military life? No, it's called CYA (Cover Your Ass). In short, you try to get as many trump cards in your own hand before someone comes along and tries to take them away from you. For the most part, I would say I have a head start on some of these people as I had to learn this game when I was at White Sands Proving Grounds.

I can see the city of Erzurum coming into view. Yep, the towns people still flock to the train station by their hundreds just to see what or who is coming into town. I'll let you in on a little secret. You wouldn't believe it, but I too have found myself going down to the train station when the train comes in just for the lack of anything better to do. The porter has placed my luggage on the platform and one of the baggage porters has gone to get my items that I shipped from Ankara. I see that the team truck has pulled in to get my baggage from the train and also the baggage from the Baggage Car. Shortly, we'll be back at the Güvenal Palas.

'Lt Morgan, when is the team due back from their field trip? I'm now told by the Third Turkish Army Headquarters Liaison Officer that they are due back Tuesday of this coming week.

'That will put them back in just three days.'

'Yeah, and then he'll be back. So much for the peaceful break.'

'But remember Sergeant Crocker, his time is getting shorter with each passing day.'

'You have a very valid point which we all should not lose sight of.'

'By the way, you did get my message to bring back a case of Old Crow whiskey, didn't you?'

'Which courier pigeon did you employ to send your message to Ankara?'

'You mean you didn't get my message?'

'Yes, I did, and the Old Crow is right here. Now since you have your Old Crow, I'll gladly accept your money in payment for your request, thank you.'

'No problem, I think that I can handle that.'

'Thanks.'

'How has Yilmaz been doing with his throat or I should say his tonsils?'

'They were acting up last week but they seem to be okay for now.'

'That kid should go to the doctor before too long and get them taken out.'

'Have you seen the butchers here in Erzurum?'

'Can't say that I have found it necessary to pay them a medical visit. After what I have heard I don't think I want to.'

'We're lucky.'

'Let's hope that our luck holds out.'

'However, I did manage to get some pills from the American Dispensary, which the doctor said would help lessen the pain should they flare up again.'

'Hopefully, I was able to do something for Yilmaz after all he has done for us.'

'True.'

Today is the day that the Guard Wizard, Colonel Jordan, makes his triumphal return to the fabled and ancient city of Erzurum. 'He'll be upset as no one will be there to greet him with blazing horns, singing praises to hosanna of having rose petals placed in his path. 'Mark my word, all of this will come back to smash him in the face, and he'll be a very pathetic whimpering person.'

'I feel sorry for him, but there is nothing in my power that I can do to alleviate that which he has already done to himself.'

'It is then you will see the common denominator of which I spoke when I first joined the team. Lt Morgan, I'll let you in on a little secret. When I start speaking like this, I really hate myself.'

'What do you mean?'

'I mean when I have these feelings, I see, note I said I see, pretty much which is coming and there is nothing I can do about it. I don't know how to control these feelings or be able to put them to good use.

That which I see, passes before my eyes like a motion picture. In short, I see the ending before the entire picture has even started. That's why I don't want anything to do with Colonel Jordan as I see him getting hurt pretty badly, not physically, but mentally and emotionally. I'll say no more on this subject, but let's just wait to see what eventuates.'

Now that Colonel Jordan is back, most of the officers seem to jump back into their little shells trying to become as inconspicuous as possible. For some it has worked, but others were caught out and would end up getting a dressing down for the slightest provocation. As for we Non-Commissioned Officers, we didn't have to worry too much, the two of us that is, as we were hardly considered members of the team or even members of the human race. I'm sure we did get under his skin but he would get back at us in many other ways. In some ways that was good, in other ways it was darn right degrading, but you never let on that any of these actions hurt you. However, be that as it may, I have learned a number of years ago one very important factor pertaining to human behaviour. That is, the only advantage other people have over you is that which you give to them. Case in point. The very first night I had joined the team and the good Colonel introduced me to the team, but added sarcastically that I sure had taken my time getting here. By using these tactics he tried to establish his advantage over me. My counter tactics by addressing his remarks and then walking out removed any of his advantages over me. This by the way, didn't do his ego any good when performed in front of his fellow officers. With this rebuff firmly planted in his subconscious mind he is not going to feel any satisfaction until he feels he has paid me back fully or even double for what I had done to him defending myself.

Being Sunday morning means that I can have a leisurely, no rush breakfast, go out later with my camera, take some pictures of the city, and in general just relax. Since I'm in no hurry I'll just wait until Yilmaz or one of the boys comes out and tell them what I would like for breakfast. In due time, Yilmaz comes out to inform us that breakfast would be served at 9.00 am by command of Colonel Jordan. Something told me that I should get up at that precise time and depart, but I didn't. I stayed and finished my cup of tea, but by that time it was much too late. Colonel Jordan with his six feet four inch frame entered the dining room and took his place at the head of the table. His first words were, 'for your dining pleasure this morning, we are having trout for breakfast.' By this time, Yilmaz and the boys were bringing in the fried trout and placing it in front of those who were seated at the table. I looked at the trout and it was looking back at me with one eye open. Fish, I despise with a passion. No way in hell am I going to eat this fish. 'Colonel Jordan,' I said while he was chomping on a large bit of fish, 'I want to thank you very much for your thoughtfulness in bringing us the fish, but I don't eat fish.' Without waiting for a reply, I excused myself from the table and went to my room. Frankly, I thought that I was going to be sick right at the table. However, as I've said before, I had reached a point in my life that I really don't like fish. I was six years old at the time and until this very day, I still dislike fish. Tell me it is physiological and I'll be the first to agree with you. However, I still do not eat seafood of any kind and I'm still very happy with myself. I waited about forty minutes or so and then I made straight for the Turkish Restaurant and had my breakfast of white cheese, jam, toast and tea. I had learned to fend for myself a long time ago and nothing had really changed. Looking up I saw Mumtaz, one of the team's interpreters coming through the door.

'Hi Mumtaz, you're a little late for breakfast aren't you?'

'Well, it's like this.'

'Like what?'

'Last night a few of us got together and we came here to dinner.' Someone suggested that we should have a small bottle of Raki.'

'Lion's milk they call it don't they? I hear tell it sure packs a powerful kick.'

'Yes, you can say that without any hesitation.'

'Continue.'

'While having dinner and talking, one thing led to another which also led to another bottle of Raki.'

'You needn't say any more. Just one look at you tells the complete story.'

'By the way, what are you up to Sergeant Crocker?'

'Well, the Colonel is back so I decided to move my ass elsewhere. Since it was such a nice day, I thought that I would take a few pictures of Erzurum in her Spring Dress.'

'If my head didn't feel so bad, I would ask to join you but it feels three times it's normal size.'

'Well you are welcome if you change your mind.'

'Thanks, but no thanks. By the way, we heard that the Chief of JAMMAT is coming out to the Third Turkish Army Headquarters for a visit.'

'Who are we?'

'One of the interpreters from Ankara called his friends here and during their conversation mentioned that the general was planning a trip next week.'

'That's nice, as nothing has been said about it to the team. I guess we know something that the Colonel doesn't know.' I looked and said nothing. Of course I could have told him that I had been informed by the general himself, but I'll let them have their little secret. 'Mumtaz, I'll see you later,' as I head up the main street to start my picture taking.

Monday night at the evening meal Colonel Jordan did his water glass tapping act to get our attention and then announced that Major General Reed would be making a visit to our team and the Third Turkish Army Headquarters in a week's time. Further, we had all better see to it that our quarters were clean and in top shape as he may just pull an inspection. The week dragged by with the usual crap hitting the fan just about every other day and people being called into the Colonel's office for a dressing-down on a wide range of subjects. The crap these people had to take from the Colonel was just unbelievable. Tomorrow, Friday, would be the big day. It was my responsibility as soon as the general's plane landed was to get his luggage and bring it to our hotel. Colonel Jordan was to be at the airport to meet him and welcome him to Erzurum and the Third Turkish Army Area. The Messing Officer was to have the bar set up and hors-d'oeuvres made and ready for the reception. Everyone had his job cut out and was expected to play it to the fullest.

On Friday morning our Signal Officer, who was our Messing Officer, received an urgent call to go out to one of his Signal Companies to alleviate a major communication problem that had arisen. He informed the Colonel and was told to take care of it and to get his ass back into Erzurum ASAP. When I was in Ankara on my courier trip, I heard some Air Force Personnel in the snack bar talking about flying and tail winds when going out East. For some reason, I made a mental note of it. General Reed, I understand, was scheduled to arrive at 1400 hours at Erzurum Airport which is about twenty minutes from our headquarters down a long dirty dusty road. About 1315 hours, Colonel Jordan called in Lt Col Laycock into his office and started chewing ass. I looked at my watch as I was ready to leave for the airport. I knocked on Colonel Jordan's door to advise him of the time and to inform him of a possible tail wind. 'Sergeant,' growled Colonel

Jordan, 'when I want any crap out of you I'll ask for it. Now shut the door and get the hell out of here.'

'Yes Sir.' After that remark, I left for the airport with my Turkish driver. To hell with him. We had no more than gotten to the airport, when I saw the general's plane coming in for a landing. There was no sign of Colonel Jordan coming down that long dirt road heading for the airport. However, the entire Third Turkish Army Brass was in place, with the brass band included, awaiting the general's arrival. Still no Colonel Jordan. As I look around, I'm the only American at the airport and I'm about to panic. Looking back up that long dirt road I now can see a vehicle heading this way but it's going to take another ten minutes to get here. The steps have been rolled up to the aircraft and the door opens. Out steps the general. The Turkish Band starts to play and the general starts down the steps. Following the general is the General's Aide-de-Camp, Captain Nelson. After the salutes are accepted all around Captain Nelson comes over to me and wants to know where Colonel Jordan is.

'Sir, you see that reddish cloud of dust coming this way?'

'Yes,'

'That's Colonel Jordan.'

'Sergeant Crocker, these are the general's luggage and mine.'

'Okay Sir, I'll take them back to our hotel.'

'Thank you very much and we'll see you later.' By this time, General Reed was making his inspection of the Honour Guard and keeping an eye on the reddish cloud of dust which has just about reached our area. As the sedan reaches the tarmac it comes to a screeching halt leaving a cloud of reddish dust heading for the Honour guard and the general's party. Shaking my head, I can see that this manoeuvre by the Colonel had trouble written all over it. Colonel Jordan rushes over to General Reed who has just completed inspecting the Honour Guard and presents his salute. Without returning his salute straight away, the general asks, 'just where in the hell have you been Jordan?' That was my cue to get the hell out of that place in a hurry. Unhesitatingly, after the luggage was placed in our vehicle, my driver and I made tracks. You might say we were like Lot in the Bible, we didn't look back. When I arrived at our hotel I asked Lt Morgan if our Messing Officer had arrived back in Erzurum. 'No he hasn't,' was his answer as he departed the hotel. Oh shit I said to myself. I had better get some of my goodies from my room and start making a few hors-d-oeuvres and in some way try to at least save the day. When all was completed, I sat them out near the bar. Even if I do say so myself, they don't look too bad or taste too bad. By this time, all of the team members were gathering in the dining room and forming some kind of a reception line. Being the lowest ranking member of the team, I was at the very end of the reception line. Colonel Jordan entered with General Reed and started making introductions to the team. This is Lt Col so 'n so this is my EX O so forth right down the line. When he got to Lt Morgan, by whom I was standing, he made that introduction, turned, and went back. There I was standing there and no introduction made. Quickly, General Reed stopped, put out his hand and said, 'Sergeant Crocker, it is sure good to see you once again. How have you been all this time?' Before I could answer the general, in that split second, you could hear all the eye balls in that room do an eyes right as General Reed shook my hand. Out of the corner of my eye I could see Colonel Jordan's heart do a flip or two. He didn't know whether to shit or go blind. Trying to get back at me, he just somehow dug his grave a little deeper. Will he never learn. Shortly thereafter, most everyone had a drink in their hand and was starting to dig into the hors-d'oeuvres. These are excellent, was the comment from General Reed. Who made them? Colonel Jordan spoke up and stated that the Messing Officer must have made them. 'No,' said Yilmaz, 'Sergeant Crocker made them when he learned that the Messing Officer hadn't returned from the Signal Company.'

'You mean that Sergeant Crocker made these delicious creations?'

'Well Jordan, I always say, if you want anything done and done correctly, just ask a Sergeant to do it.' Yak, there went another nail in Colonel Jordan's coffin was my passing thought. He will never learn to shut his mouth and let the information be fed to him. No, he the good Colonel has to be the perpetrator in all things, even those he knows absolutely nothing about. Frankly, I feel very sorry for him. The ensuing evening meal, thank God, turned out to be fantastic, and no fish was served. The one thing I did notice was that the other officers on the team after Major General Reed seemingly broke the ice barrier and were looking at me in a different light. No longer were they afraid to speak with me, but they even smiled. In their eyes, I had just been elevated to another plain, but the fact was they had opened their hearts and not their eyes to me.

Saturday morning was the day that the official party were going to go out to some of the border units to inspect them. For those who had to go on this inspection tour, breakfast was being served two hours earlier. However, I decided to remain in bed and go to my favourite Turkish Restaurant later in the morning and have my white cheese, jam, toast and tea. After all the excitement yesterday who needs any more thrills. A nice casual breakfast would be just what the doctor would order. Tomorrow by this time, the general and Captain Nelson will be heading back to Ankara and perhaps peace, such as it is, should return to the Third Turkish Army Headquarters and the Field Training Team 3-A. Somehow, I have a gut feeling inside that a number of things have been changed and things will not revert to that which they were in the past. What a difference a day makes.

Now that General Reed's visit is past history, it is only one week before Colonel Jordan departs FTT 3-A and heads to Ankara to take up his new duties in JAMMAT Headquarters. Since he didn't come up smelling like roses during General Reed's visit, I somehow wonder just what fate awaits him in the big city? There is plenty of time to think about that later. Now there are plans afoot to hold a big farewell get together with the Turkish and American Military Personnel on the front lawn of the Third Turkish Army Headquarters. Our American Executive Officer is planning it and from what I understand, it will be a cold buffet with all the trimmings. They even plan on having a bar set up for those who desire something stronger than beer. The invitations have been printed and it is my job to obtain the Turkish Officers' names who are being invited to the farewell. It should go without saying that neither Sergeant Bilman nor myself were even considered on the invitation list. To hell with them, we'll throw our very own 'Thank God he's leaving party' and invite our own guests. It's a thought, and not too bad at that. We'll just have to give it a little more thought.

'Sergeant Crocker, have you completed addressing the invitations yet?'

'Sir, I have just two left and then I'll have completed the 75 invitations you wanted addressed.' Silly old fuck. He gives you all these invitations to address, sends you upstairs twice to get information for him, plus taking messages on the phone for him and now he expects everything to be accomplished in just forty minutes. I wonder just what slave farm he used to manage. I should worry as the time is drawing closer each day for his departure. 'Here you are Sir, these invitations are now completed.'

'Good,' he said, 'now we can start working on the menu. Now write this down. We'll have some roast beef, chicken, two different kinds of salad, bread rolls, butter, fruit and cake.'

'That should be plenty Sir, if everyone shows up.'

'What do you mean by that remark, if everyone shows up?'

'Just a figure of speech, Sir.' Yak, he sure didn't like that remark. This affair has been planned pretty close all the way around. That is to say, on Friday afternoon at 1.00 p.m. the luncheon is to take place and Colonel Jordan is to leave on Saturday afternoon on the train for Ankara. He didn't want to take THY (Turkish Airline) as he doesn't like flying. To be sure, he'll have a very beautiful trip to Ankara at this time of the year.

'Sergeant Crocker, are you and Sergeant Bilman going to help serve today at the farewell gathering for Colonel Jordan?'

'Hell no, Lt Morgan, Sergeant Bilman and I were not even invited to attend, let alone play waiters. As a matter of interest, the two of us are making plans to be doing other things, so please do not worry about our welfare.' To be honest, we haven't made any plans at all. However, should the rumours be correct, which the interpreters told us, well, I for one just don't want to be near the place. With the time nearing 1.00 p.m. Colonel Jordan leaves his room at the Güvenal Palas to make his way to the Third Turkish Army Headquarters and his farewell party. The one thing I had noticed on the invitations that the Executive Officer had printed, he forgot to have RSVP printed on the invitations. Since this was his show, who was I to tell him of the social graces on invitations. Further, since my arrival at the team, that Sergeants didn't get paid to think, so I just let it go. The entire American Team minus Sergeant Bilman and I had gathered under the canopy waiting for the Turkish counterpart to join them. Time started slipping away, but no Turkish Military Personnel had showed up. Trying to keep a brave face, Colonel Jordan told the American Officers to dig in and help themselves to the food. Lt Morgan went into our office and called the Güvenal Palas and told Sergeant Bilman and I to get our asses down to the party. It must be true, I said, no one showed up. We arrived in about six or seven minutes and only the American Team was present. My God, what a big slap in the face for Colonel Jordan. Yes, he in many ways asked for it, and true to form, they obliged in kind. What a sad picture of that man sitting before me. The once brave face he was wearing has slowly slipped away and the lines seemed deeper than ever

73

before. With the one last look around, he got out of his chair, walked to his sedan, and drove away.

The following afternoon, Saturday, we all gathered at the Erzurum train station to see him off to Ankara. He appeared somewhat better, outwardly, but inwardly you could see that nothing had really changed and he was carrying a personal deep hurt. I wanted to tell him, 'Sir, this is how other people felt when you ran rough shod over them, caring little for their feelings while fuelling your own ego.' but the train was slowly moving out of the station.

Sunday morning breaks forth with peaceful vibrations emanating all around the Güvenal Palas like a very fine mystic spray emanating from another world. Like the children of Israel we were led out of bondage and delivered into the hands of Colonel Barlow, our new Team Chief. Our new Team Chief, Colonel Barlow, seems completely different from Colonel Jordan. For openers, he seems very approachable, not bad looking for a man of his age. He seems most sincere, six feet three inches tall, with striking steel blue eyes, solid build and a genuine interest in his men and his mission. However, some of these quick observations will have to be proven with the passage of time. Above all, he seems to have a good sense of humour which is most essential in an assignment like this.

'Good morning Lt Morgan,'

'I don't know just how good it is, as my poor head doesn't feel the best.'

'I know, as you didn't sound like you were feeling any pain upon your arrival from the Turkish Officers' party last night.'

'Damn good party, what I remember of it. Sergeant Crocker, there is something that I have wanted to again speak to you about concerning Colonel Jordan.'

'What's on your mind Lt Morgan?'

'We had spoken on this subject some time ago, but it has been on my mind. You had said something about a common denominator and that something was going to happen to Colonel Jordan to hurt him very much. It came to pass you know.'

'Yes, I know.'

'My question is, just how did you know that something like this was going to happen so far in advance?'

'Putting it this way Lt Morgan, I could just see that which was to happen. Shall we just leave it at that?'

'Okay, if you say so. I guess I had better get something for my throbbing head before it falls off.'

'By the way, have you noticed Yilmaz the last couple of days?'

'Now that you have mentioned it, I have. It must be his tonsils playing up again. One of these days before too long he is going to have to have a tonsillectomy performed before he has very real problems.'

'There is a private doctor just up around the corner from here that does that type of surgery.'

'If it is necessary Lt Morgan, I'll go with Yilmaz to have it done and if necessary, I'll pay for it. I just can't stand to see the poor kid in so much pain. Tomorrow is Monday, so I'll just hang back and speak to Yilmaz and see what he would like to do. After that, we'll get our heads together and see what we can come up with.'

Everyone has departed for the office, so I'll go and see Yilmaz.

'Good morning Yilmaz, and how do you feel today?'

'Not too good Sir.'

'Yes, I can see that your throat is all swollen up.'

'I used all of the pills that you brought back from Ankara which really helped.'

'Do you feel up to going to see the doctor just up the street today?'

'I don't want to go to the doctor by myself as it scares the hell out of me.'

'Okay, I have spoken to Lt Morgan and he told me that if you wanted to go to the doctor, that I could take time off and go with you. Would that be okay?'

'Well . . .'

'Yilmaz, I know how you feel, but I'll be right there with you at all times. What time would you like to go and see him?'

'We'll go just as soon as I shave and get myself dressed.'

'I'll wait in my room, so as soon as you are ready, give me a call.'

We ascended two flights of stairs to the doctor's office located on the second floor of the rather old building. Upon entering the doctor's reception room one sure could have a feeling of being cramped or even a case of claustrophobia in such close quarters. The room was approximately eight feet long and about eight feet wide. The ceiling didn't seem much higher. If you got more than two people in the room at the same time, you would have a crowd. Shortly the doctor came out of the surgery which joins his reception room. He invited Yilmaz in but I followed. He didn't know what to say, so he said nothing. After the initial examination he told Yilmaz that he held his surgery on every Tuesday. He said that he would operate on Yilmaz on Tuesday which is tomorrow. I asked Yilmaz for all the details including the cost of the operation plus if the doctor made any house calls to see his patient after surgery. Yes he did, if he thought it was necessary. I said to Yilmaz, ask the good doctor if I thought it was necessary that he comes to see you if he would come? While Yilmaz asked the question, I was looking at the doctor right squarely in the eye and didn't flinch. He told Yilmaz, oh yes he would come if I called him. 'Good, we'll see you tomorrow.' With that we departed the doctor's office.

'Sergeant Crocker, I think that the doctor got a little scared when you looked so hard at him.'

'Good,' I replied, 'maybe he'll do a better job.' At 9.00 am the following morning both Yilmaz and I were in the doctor's office at the appointed time. Since I was going to work after the operation, I had my nice freshly starched summer uniform on with the short sleeves. We waited for about ten minutes and the doctor asked us into his surgery. He had Yilmaz take a seat in what seemed like a barber's chair minus part of the head rest. I looked quickly around the room to see if I could find the steriliser for the medical equipment but only saw a kerosene stove over to one side of the room with a pot sitting on it with boiling water with steam coming up from it. There was something in the pot, but I couldn't make out just what it was. For all I knew, it could have been his lunch cooking. Further, I didn't see him wash his hands and that worried the hell out of me. He told Yilmaz when the time came for me to stand beside him and hold Yilmaz's head in a given position. Would you believe that I'm now the doctor's assistant and I'm not even getting remunerated for my services rendered. Now, and only now, can I fully understand why Yilmaz would be scared out of his wits with such goings on. With me there, he at least had a fighting chance. As the doctor moved slowly towards the boiling pot on top of the kerosene stove, I watched him closely and followed his every move. He picks up his forceps and takes his surgical tonsil equipment out of the boiling water and places it on a towel to his left. Shaking my head, I can only assume that this is sterilisation at its best in Eastern Turkey. When the tonsil instrument cooled down so he could hold it, he took it in his right hand and gave me instructions to hold Yilmaz's head very still as it was going to hurt. Prior to all of this, there was just one small shot of anaesthetic administered when we first went into the doctor's office, nothing more. He then placed the instrument into Yilmaz's mouth, pulled back on the handle, snip, and one tonsil was cut out. He placed that on the table. He then went back and got the second one. By this time, blood had squirted and sprayed all over my arm and on to my uniform as Yilmaz sharply turned his head in pain. Blood was spilling forth from Yilmaz's mouth, but the good doctor had the situation well in hand. He pulled a round clear plastic bottom vacuum cleaner out of the corner, turned it on, and placed a special home made suction nozzle into Yilmaz's mouth which sucked out the blood and saliva, spinning it around like a merry-go-round on the sides of the clear plastic vacuum cleaner's bottom. God knows that was just plain sickening.

Unbeknown to me, the fun part of this operation was about to unfold. When the bulk of the bleeding stopped, the doctor had Yilmaz and I move back to the reception room. Let's face it, there was no other place where we could be seated. The small recovery room would have been great, but no such luck. There were four people in the reception room all gooking at us when we entered. At first, I didn't realise that I was still covered with Yilmaz's blood and Yilmaz was still spitting out blood. I'm sure that would send chills up and down their spines to say the least. That was a fact of life and at the time there wasn't anything we could do about it. They could have looked away, but no, they choose only to gook. Finally the doctor came out of his office and took two of the people into his surgery. While sitting in the reception room a very surprising fact was slowly coming to light. The anaesthetic which the doctor had administered was only now taking effect. My God, Yilmaz had gone through the entire operation without the benefit of the anaesthetic which was administered. I now understand why he pulled and jerked as hard as he did. When I realised this, my heart went out to him. He suffered the entire pain of the operation. Now, and only now, is he beginning to get relaxed and sleepy and I have to walk him three blocks home to the Güvenal Palas. You say, why not get a taxi? The only taxis they have are horse-drawn carriages. It would take two men and a boy to get Yilmaz into one. Further, when the Turkish Citizens see me with a bleeding Turkish young man, and me covered with blood, they may not stop and ask what happened. Many of these people are village people and they don't stop and ask questions. They just assume. Further, with Yilmaz in his present condition, he could do little in telling them that I was helping him and not hurting him. The doctor came out once again and seemed a little surprised that we were still there. I guess he thought that we were bad for his business. After our short wait, Yilmaz said that he felt like he could try making it back to the Güvenal Palas. Slowly I got him to his feet, but he seemed hesitant and wobbly on his feet. The fact was the we couldn't stay in the doctor's office too much longer, as more people came in and we were taking up their space. With my arm around Yilmaz and his arm over my shoulder, we started our move down the stairs. I would take the first step and let him put his entire weight on me as we slowly took the steps one by one. After we had gotten down the first flight of steps, I sat him down on the steps and let him rest as well as myself. The second flight of steps seemed a bit easier than the first. When we reached the street, we had another breather. Now, there are only three short blocks to negotiate and we should be home free. Out of the corner of my eye, I can see a few people just across the street stopping and having a long hard look at the situation. My thoughts were, as long as they are only looking and not saying anything the better my chances of getting Yilmaz home without incident. Luck was on our side, as the people only looked and watched us moving towards the Güvenal Palas. Reaching the front door, I rang the door bell. I waited and waited, but no one answered the door bell. Finally, I told Yilmaz to hang on to me as I would try to get my key out of my pocket and unlock the door. After nearly dropping him on to the ground, I managed to get my key out and open the door. Now, my only problem was is that I had to negotiate Yilmaz up one flight of turning stairs. This should be relatively easy as we just came down two flights of stairs. Not so. Yilmaz's feet started up the stairs, but not Yilmaz. He is now at a forty-five degree angle and his feet are going higher. However, the rest of Yilmaz is still on the bottom floor with me and his arms wrapped around my neck. Slowly, I got his feet back down on the bottom floor without falling. Suddenly the front door opens and it is one of the other Turkish Soldiers that works in our hotel just came in. Thank God for small favours. With him on one side and me on the other, we finally got Yilmaz upstairs and into his bed. Shortly thereafter Yilmaz was fast asleep. I then went to my room to take off my uniform and soak it in cold water to help remove the blood stains. I was sure a mess. Since this project took longer than expected, I decided just to take a shower, get my new uniform put together and just wait for lunch.

With the passage of time, Yilmaz was a new person once again and assumed his regular duties even better than before. He now felt secure and realised that people really cared about his welfare and the welfare of the others.

As the months rolled by, it became apparent that I was suffering from a hernia on my left side. My tour of duty on the team was very near being completed, so Colonel Barlow suggested that I go to the JAMMAT Dispensary, a six man bed complex at Cebeci, and have the operation to get it repaired. By this time, most of the team members had all rotated and new members were coming in and taking their places. However, since I was so close to my normal rotating date, I didn't see too many problems with that. The only slight problem was to find a place to live in Ankara. After five days in a hotel, I finally found a place in Bahçelievler to live. It was much too big for me, a two storey house, but the people who wanted to rent it were going to be exchange teachers in the United States and just had to rent it. In the garden room was a beautiful grand piano in all its glory. Just what was I going to do with a grand piano was beyond me. However, fate had things pretty well planned in advance just waiting for me to come and join the party. To me the most important thing was to get to the Dispensary, have my operation, get back on my feet, and get back to work. According to my landlady, the most important thing in the house was the telephone. A special addition to my contract was, before the rent was even paid, I must make sure that the telephone bill was paid first. In order to obtain a telephone during 1957 in Turkey, you had to be high up in the government or know someone who was. Otherwise, there was no telephone to be had at any price. By Turkish standards, if you had a telephone, you were considered very wealthy. In my case, I was considered very lucky. However, you had to ring the operator to get connected to a number you were calling. Not all the time, but sometimes you didn't come across a very understanding operator and it was just plain work to call someone. All conversations were in Turkish so you had to give them the numbers in Turkish. Some operators were most helpful while others would just pull the plug.

After one week, I was finally settled into my home in Bahçelievler so I presented myself in Cebeci at the US Dispensary for admission. Since it was only a six man bed Dispensary there weren't too many people there. Later, oh yes, later, I also found out that they had two beds set aside for expecting new mothers. It was only a plywood partition which divided the two sections. They had the usual exams checking this and that to see if you were physically fit to undergo the operation. Your exam wouldn't be complete without the usual vampires extracting your life blood. Needless, to say, I really hate needles. After the examination, a young 1st Lieutenant Doctor Stein came in to have a chat with me. Frankly, I think I was older than he, but that carried little weight as he was the doctor. He had another look at my hernia on my left side and pushed a little here and a little there, all the time shaking his head. Further, there were three nurses on duty at the Dispensary, but not all at the same time. The one that was on duty today I nicknamed her 1st Lieutenant *Miss Efficiency* as she wanted the poor ward-men to have everything accomplished tomorrow by today. She was even faultfinding with the sick patients and other Dispensary volunteer staff. I made up my mind that if she locked horns with me, though she was an officer, she would come off second best.

Around midnight the nice nurse Louise, she too was a 1st Lieutenant came around and said that Doctor Stein told her to tell me that he would commence my operation in the morning and I could have nothing to drink from this time forward. I thanked her and tried to get some sleep. With news like that, sleep took wing leaving me wide awake and full of nervous questions. For me, morning came all too quickly and I'm sure that my blood pressure, if taken then, would confirm my fears. They wheeled me into this small room which doubles for an operating room and a delivery room. They lifted me across onto the operating table. Looking quickly around, something doesn't seem just right to me. There is a woman in the operating room dressed in a surgical gown and mask standing on my right side. I asked the doctor who this woman was and he told me it was Doctor Suzan. 'Oh,' he continued, 'she is going to assist me with your operation. In a way.' he said.

'What do you mean when you say in a way?'

'The fact is Sergeant Crocker, she cannot touch you being you are an American citizen and she is a Turkish Citizen. She is here to assist me with the spinal injection.'

'Hold it right there Doctor Stein. No one here even mentioned a spinal injection and suddenly I'm to have a spinal.'

'We thought it would be best for you.'

'Excuse me Doctor Stein, but who in the hell is we?'

'I spoke with Doctor Suzan through the interpreter last night and we settled for the spinal injection.'

'I'm so very happy that all was settled without my consent.'

'Obviously, the procedures have advanced to the point that there is no turning back.'

'Further Doctor Stein, you look like you are on the tired side to start with. Must be too much work.' I'm now turned on my left side exposing my entire back to Doctor Suzan. She picks up something that looks like a pointer you would use in a classroom to point out something on a class blackboard. The point is dipped into a liquid amber solution and she moves closer towards me. It is cold, as it touches a point in the middle of my back on the spinal column and I have the eerie feeling that is where they are going to shove the needle into my spine. Doctor Suzan moves away from me and Doctor Stein takes her position with a large syringe pointed in my back's direction. From the look of it, he's going to prise my spinal column apart. Nurse Hollingsworth has taken her position which is at my head. Now the wardsman has joined the happy group and he will be holding my legs. I somehow get the feeling that this little episode is going to hurt like hell. I say to myself, if it is not true, why are so many people starting to hold different parts of my body. While waiting for the fatal jab of the needle, I can hear the little children with their mums in the hallway where they are holding morning Sick Call. The only thing I can think of at the moment a little more primitive than this place, is the doctor's office in Erzurum. Why did I ever let myself be talked into having the surgery done here when I could have gone to a big US Medical Hospital in Germany. Frankly, I think that I should have my head examined prior to my hernia operation.

Doctor Stein moves closer and in his hand he is holding a huge syringe with an extra size needle attached to the end of it. Of course, because it's going to be jabbed into my spinal column it seems extra large. Medically speaking, I'm sure that it meets all the specifications of being a regular size needle, but it sure in hell looks larger when it is about to be jabbed into me. With the initial jab I have a normal reaction and stiffen up. Oh God, it seems like he has a crow bar and trying to prise my spinal column apart to let the needle in. Nurse Hollingsworth is trying to console me, but at that moment the pain is far too severe for such tactics. The pain is now excruciating, but still he pushes on. I suddenly hear Dr Suzan say Dur! Dur! In Turkish I know that it means stop, stop. I didn't feel the needle coming out, but boy I know it's been there. Slowly, I begin to feel a numbness in the toe of my right leg as the anaesthetic starts to take hold. Now it has taken over the toe of my left leg. Gradually, it works its way up both legs until it has reached my mid section. No, it doesn't stop there. Slowly, it has reached the nipples on my chest and has shown no signs of stopping. If they are showing signs of being concerned, I wonder just what in hell they thought I was feeling? About two inches past the nipples on my chest the numbness stopped. During this time, Dr Stein had a pin in his hand and was using me as a human pincushion and asking me, 'Did I feel this?' Each time I answered in the affirmative he would pick out another position to jab me. I was beginning to get a bit concerned for myself and my blood pressure only proved it. 'Just remain calm,' Dr Stein said over and over again. I had a funny feeling just wondering if he was trying to convince me or himself. When the anaesthetic stopped moving upwards he wiped the perspiration from his face and just sat there a couple of minutes. Finally, I was rolled over on my back, the bottom part of my PJ's was removed and I was as naked as a jay bird. Next came a generous splashing of iodine on my left side where the surgical instrument was to be plunged into my body. If I ever wanted to be somewhere else, it was surely at that precise time. However, luck wasn't with me and the knife was plunged into my quivering body and I mean quivering. You see, they forgot to put up the little wire frame and a towel over it to block my view. Thus, I saw the knife pierce my skin with the blood starting to slowly trickle down my side. Their mistake was quickly found when they saw my blood pressure starting to take off. The frame was quickly raised and a towel placed over it. Slowly, my blood pressure started to drop. Funny thing this human body. It stands for no foolishness. Nurse Hollingsworth kept telling me that the needle which was placed into my arm and the little bag and the plastic tubing to which it was attached was a very tasty steak dinner. I looked at her and told her that I thought she was a very nice person, but please don't try to make funnies at a time like this. Frankly, it wasn't the time nor the place and furthermore, I wasn't hungry. She just smiled and let it pass. I can see a bit of perspiration starting to appear on the forehead of the good doctor. This of course leads me to believe that he is getting down to the serious business of the operation. With a tug here and a tug there I can sure feel that something is going on. I hope that he has raised or elevated the scrotum as the blood will seek its lowest level. Why worry about it. If he has fine, if not, it's too late to worry about it now. Anyway, a red scrotum could be a real focal point for conversation. The good doctor is now taking off his surgical gloves so it would appear that he has finished playing seamstress with my inner and outer sides. I feel very tired and thankful that the operation is over with as they lift me on to the trolley to move me back to my bed in the next room. Sick Call is now over with and the little children and their mums and dads have long departed the Dispensary and the hallway is once again quiet. When they are here, they are noisy and the kids keep running into the ward and causing havoc with the patients. A good smack on the rump would sure bring that to a screeching halt. It seems like some mother's today, have little concern for the action of their children. I just can't help think what it will be like in ten to twenty years from now. Heaven forbid. Well, they have dumped me into my bed the same way they took me out of the operation room, just covered with a sheet. 'What was that on the radio?'

'It's about the Russians.'

'What about the Russians?'

'They have launched a satellite orbiting around the earth called Sputnik.'

'Well, they beat us into space.' The way I'm feeling at present, I could orbit around the earth and care less about it.

Having placed my wash cloth over my face, I'll try to get some rest and perhaps have a nap if possible and hope the pain will go away. I was feeling somewhat better until someone lifted my wash cloth and asked if I was okay.

'Yes, I'm okay Dr Stein.'

'I was just checking.' With my answer, he leaves. Shortly, Nurse Hollingsworth comes in and wants to give me an injection to ease me over the pain when the anaesthetic starts to wear off. 'Nurse Hollingsworth, can I ask you a question?'

'Sure, I'll try to answer it.'

'Just why is Dr Stein so interested in me and how I'm doing?'

'Well, frankly, I don't know if I should answer that question or not. However, since you asked the question openly, I'll tell you openly. Dr Stein spent most of last night reading his medical books learned how to perform the hernia operation which he performed on you this morning.'

'I'll be go to hell. It's such a grand feeling to know that you have just been a human guineapig for a doctor who didn't know his ass from third base and knowing you have just helped him complete his medical course. Oh shit, I pray that he got everything back in the right order.'

'Sergeant Crocker, please don't tell him I told you. No Nurse Hollingsworth, it's our little secret.'

'Isn't it about time that they brought some food around this place! Garsh, a guy could starve to death.'

'First, you must take your mineral oil.'

'My what?'

'Your mineral oil. That will help things slide down better when they pass the hernia repaired section.'

'I'm so happy about that.'

'Well, you will be when the times comes. Just wait until you have your first bowel movement. You'll be more than happy that you have had your mineral oil.'

I see that I have on my tray some nice mashed potatoes with butter, mashed carrots, jello and a glass of milk. That is sure a far cry from the steak dinner Nurse Hollingsworth was trying to sell me when I was on the operating table. She was just trying to build up my hopes. What a rotten joke to play on a person in my situation. With the pain in my side and being propped up, I managed to get the mashed potatoes, mashed carrots and jello down. I can't say that it was the most outstanding meal I've ever had, but under the circumstances I should stop my bellyaching and accept that which was.

I see that they have admitted a rather pregnant-looking woman and placed her in the operating room as there is no ward for women. What separates her from the male patients is a three quarter inch plywood partition and that is it. Between the two rooms, you can almost hear a pin drop. I just pray that she doesn't go into labour until I've had a good night's rest. After that she can do whatever she wants. I see that Nurse First Lieutenant *Miss Efficiency*, that's the name I have given her, has just come on duty and will spend the night with us until 8.30 am in the morning. She is a bitch of the first water and not even the doctors here can stand her. One day, she is going to get belted between the eyes and wonder why. That's enough thought wasted on her.

'Good night honey.'

'Good night Ayse.' I forget to tell you that Ayse is the cleaning woman who works here in the dispensary and is a sweet, jolly old lady in her fifties. She would weigh in around 220 pounds and stands about 5 feet 5 inches tall. You might say she was on the heavy side but she is still a sweet jolly old lady. She would wear her shoes to work, but changed into an old pair of sandals which flip flopped all day long wherever she'd walk. 1st Lt *Miss Efficiency* didn't like her, but then again who liked *Miss Efficiency*. Every morning Ayse would bring fresh flowers to every patient and place them in a glass of water by our bedside. This she did faithfully every morning five days a week. The only thing Lt *Miss Efficiency* would bring was discontent among the other staff and the patients.

I had just received my painkilling injection and was dropping off to sleep when all of a sudden we heard a bloodcurdling scream from the operating room. Oh my God, it's the woman expecting the baby. You could hear a buzz all over the ward. First on the scene was, you guessed it, 1st Lt *Miss Efficiency* who told us all to be quiet and go back to sleep. Who was she trying to kid. That scream scared the piss out of all of us, some more than others. Things had settled down somewhat when she gave forth with another blast. This was the pattern which was to last all night until 5.00 am. The last time she yelled was 'Oh doctor, take the damn thing out of me.' I just laughed and wondered if anyone had ever told her about the birds and the bees and how that little thing had gotten into her in the first place. By this time, none of us had had any sleep and we weren't feeling to crash hot. The next thing I remember were the little children running in and out of our ward being screamed at by their mommies and daddies. To top it off, Corporal Adams, a wardsman, was being harassed by 1st Lt *Miss Efficiency* to hurry and get all the linen on the beds changed and beds made before the doctor and she came on their morning inspection tour. I feel my blanket being pulled off my bed and knew my sheets were next. Not having any strength in my arms to hold on to my sheets, I placed it in my mouth and held it with my teeth. Corporal Adams had my sheet from the foot of the bed and I wouldn't let go from the top. Suddenly appearing on the scene was, you know who, 1st Lt *Miss Efficiency*. She started giving Corporal Adams a royal chewing out because he hadn't completed making my bed. At that point, I spat out the sheet and asked the 1st Lt to hold it.

'You can't tell me to hold it,' she shouted at me. 'I'm in charge here and you have to do what I say. I'll have your court martialled.'

'Lt., shut you damn mouth before I get out of bed in my condition and shut it for you.'

'You have threatened me with physical violence.' Everyone in the ward burst out laughing. Just how much physical violence could I do to her when I couldn't even at this point get out of bed. She dropped the front end of the sheet and looked at me.

'Lt.,' I said, 'if you take this sheet, I'm left here just like the day I entered the world. I have nothing on. Further, what about all the little kids and running around in the ward, do you want them to see a nude man?'

'Where are your pyjamas?'

'I'm just the way they brought me out of surgery and dumped me here naked. You know everything, you tell me where my pyjamas are?'

'I'm going to report you to the doctor for the way you have treated me and the things you have said to me.'

'You just do that, as the doctor has been standing there all the time you have been rampaging and raving. Go on, tell him.' With that, she turned around and saw the doctor standing there and departed in one big huff. She fully knew that she had overstepped her bounds and was caught red handed. You just don't yell at wardsmen and above all patients, let alone surgical patients. Finally, Aysa, the domestic help came to my rescue and helped me into my pyjamas. After all that display of words and actions, I finally let Corporal Adams have my sheets and didn't have to play Sally Rand with them any longer. Come to think of it, Sally Rand only used ostrich feathers and had nothing to do with bed sheets. I'm sure you've gotten the message.

After all that excitement I truly feel very tired and sore in the area of my operation and I hope that I haven't dropped a stitch. Taking my wash cloth I place it over my face and try to get a little shut eye. I no more than drop off to sleep and someone removes my wash cloth.

'Doctor.'

'How are you feeling Sergeant Crocker?'

'To tell the truth Doctor Stein, I'm tired, sleepy and sore. As you know we didn't get very much sleep last night with that woman screaming all night.'

'By the way, she had a 7 pound 5 ounce baby boy.'

'That's nice doctor, but all of us here still remain tired and sleepy.'

The following morning Aysa comes in and seemed very sad. 'Honey', she started off, 'I no bring you pretty flowers today.' Every day, she would bring us all new flowers for our glass of water by our bed.

I said, 'Aysa, that's okay,' and was willing to drop the subject there.

'Honey,' she continued, 'you no want to know why I no bring you flowers today?'

'Okay Aysa, why you no bring us flowers today.'

'This morning, the policeman stopped me and told me that I could not go into ladies' yard to get flowers.'

'My God,' I said to myself, she had been stealing flowers to bring us fresh flowers each day. It all goes to prove one thing, that some people's hearts are far larger than their pocket-books.

Ten days later I was released from the Dispensary and returned to my home in Bahçelievler where I spent another seven days before I had to return to work. During my time at home, a Mr Edward Jones a Consultant on Asian Theatre Affairs for the International Cultural Exchange Service of the American National Theatre and Academy come to call on me. He had gotten my name from JAMMAT, noting that I was a choir director. When he came into my home he noted that I had a grand piano in my garden room which seemed to answer his question. He asked me to be the musical director for the stage play *Oklahoma!*. After a lot of discussion I finally said that I would do it. Little did I realise then that in my later years in Turkey that this stage production presented on 26th December 1957 would hold a key in later years.

Chapter Four

During 1963 and 1964 Archbishop Makarios had brought much bitter conflict to Cyprus between Greece, Turkey, Great Britain, United States and the United Nations over his policy for Enosis or Union with Greece. The stance which Turkey took concerning these conflicts not only strained the country's friendship with the United States but also its alliance with Greece.

Fighting between Greek and Turkish Cypriots broke out in December 1963. The United Nations sent peace-keeping forces to Cyprus but Greek Cypriots still fought on and tried to take the coastal area still held by the Turkish Cypriots. By August 1964 and after many demonstrations held in Turkey, the Turkish Air Force finally bombed Greek strongholds in the area. This action sent a strong message to Athens and Nicosia that the Turks have had enough and were willing to take a stand. The United States under the leadership of President L B Johnston didn't really or fully understand the situation nor did his advisers. It took a lot of fancy and fast foot work to bring these two NATO countries back under control. However, neighbouring countries such as Egypt and Russia wanted or sought Cypriots, under Greece, for their own interests. Egypt for it's fight with Israel and Russia for its hopeful disintegration against NATO and its southern flank. Quickly, as Master Plan had to be devised and placed into operation. Thus, *Operation Unsuspecting* was born which focused between the United States and Turkey. Would it achieve its desired potential? Only time would tell.

After spending 22 months in Turkey on a 24 month tour of duty, I was transferred back to Fort Bliss, Texas to the Air Defence Command. Being stationed so close to White Sands Proving Ground I made a trip there to see if my good friend Herb was still stationed there. As luck would have it, Herb was gone as well as General Hall. I remained at Fort Bliss for about eight months and then put in for a transfer through Washington DC to return to JAMMAT in Turkey. Strangely enough, it was approved very quickly and a month later I found myself back in Turkey. Needless to say, I was much better prepared in every department and no, I didn't stay in the Tourist Hotel. I checked into the Bulivar Hotel near JAMMAT. During the time I was out of Turkey, they changed the headquarters name and brought in many more military personnel. The new name was Joint United States Military Mission Aid Turkey, or JUSMMAT. On Monday morning I went to the Army Section of JUSMMAT and reported in for duty. While there, the Army Section Sergeant Major asked me if I was going to be looking for an apartment? I told him 'yes.'

'I'll save you time and money as there is going to be a vacant unit in about a week's time.' The location was excellent and only about a five minute walk to the headquarters. Further, if I wanted to save some money, I could move in with him and two other Sergeants in the ground floor unit until my unit became vacant. I took him up on his offer and moved in on Wednesday after work. His address was Gülözü Sokak. My address was to be Gülözü Sokak Unit 7. Yes, with that address I was considered on Embassy Row. Later that evening, Ray, the Sergeant Major, called across the street to some people and wanted to know if they wanted to come over for a drink. Since there wasn't too much social life in our section of town, they accepted. I was introduced to Mrs De Cario who was an American from Waterbury, Connecticut. Her husband followed and I was introduced to him. His name was Armando. He spoke English with a very heavy accent. Later, I found out that he was Count De Cario from Rome and Mrs De Cario was Elaine who was a real live Contessa. I went to the kitchen and helped Ray with the drinks. From what I could see from the kitchen Elaine had a rather nice figure. I would say a hour-glass figure. You know, just the right amount of sand at the top and the right amount of sand at the bottom. I would venture a guess that she was about 5 feet 6 or 7 inches tall. Armando was thin as a rail and about 5 feet 9 inches tall. In a good wind storm, he would be long gone.

'This is for you Mrs De Cario,' I said.

'Please call me Elaine.'

'Thank you.'

Ray handed Armando his drink. It would appear that Armando had a head start on all of us. Since he works as the First Secretary at the

90

Mexican Consul General's Office, they sometimes get off work a little early. Elaine I found out teaches English at one of the private Turkish Schools as she speaks both languages very well. The conversation was lively, but I was tired. However, I couldn't go to bed as the couch was my bed and they were sitting on it. Time did pass and they finally went home and I jumped into my bed.

Five days later, I moved out of Ray's place and moved into my Unit. Since my household goods had not arrived, I was able to borrow a few things from JUSMMAT Headquarters which enabled me to set up housekeeping. I went to Ulus and did some good old fashioned hard bargaining on the purchase of two beautiful hand made Isparta Rugs. It must be worth it, as I saved 975 Turkish Lira, the equivalent around $115.00 US dollars. I was sure pooped after that marathon endurance contest with the shopkeeper. I drank so much tea during this bargaining session to float a couple of battleships. The point being is to see who can outlast whom. Since I spent all my money obtaining my purchase, I didn't have any money left to get them home. The shopkeeper didn't seem to care, as he obtained a horse and wagon to take them to my unit. How did I get home? I had fifty kurus in my pocket so I took the local bus system.

About a month later, Ray, our Sergeant Major in the Army Section left for home in the United States and a Master Sergeant Lunday replaced him. Now that Ray was gone, it sort of fell upon me to keep the relationship going with Elaine and Armando. In a number of ways, they helped me and I returned the favour. It was one evening when I was in Armando and Elaine's home that I found out that Elaine used to be in charge of a department in one of Istanbul's hospitals. Just what she did, I never knew but I learned that she worked with WHO (World Health Organisation). That all ended when she married Armando and moved to Ankara. To help supplement the family income, she took up teaching.

Since Ray has left the country, it seems that I was elected to fill the void in our neighbourhood so far as Armando and Elaine were concerned. It was nice to have people you could talk to after a day's work without talking shop. They would visit me and I would visit them and we became friends as time passed.

'Carl, oh Carl, I'm up here.' Looking around, upward and across, the little street, I can see Elaine hanging over the balcony calling to me.

'Hi, up there, what's happening?'

'I forgot to ask you yesterday if you were available to attend a dinner party on Saturday night?'

'What?'

'Hold on Carl, I'll be right down.'

'Hi Elaine,' as I give her a kiss on the cheek.

'Yea Carl, Madam Nur, you know her, she's the Turkish Ambassador's wife and she is giving a dinner party on Saturday night. She asked Armando to ask you if you would like to attend. Armando didn't see you, so I thought that I had better ask you.'

'What type of a dinner party is she holding and who will be there?'

'She didn't tell Armando, but only to ask you. I'm sure she has some ulterior motive in mind.'

'Elaine, I've never met the lady in question, but I have seen her on a number of occasions and from her back balcony and she has even waved to me.'

'It seems that she is a very friendly lady.'

'That's nice Elaine, but just how friendly? Further, what do I have to do for my supper, sing?'

'Maybe even something better, who knows.'

'Have Armando inform Madam Nur that I would be most delighted to attend her dinner party on Saturday night. By the way Elaine,what are you planning on wearing?'

'I'll call my seamstress and have her run something a little special up for me. Her creations are excellent, and they don't cost the earth.'

'I guess I'll wear my dark suit and bow tie. What do you think?'

'Sounds perfectly logical to me.'

'What is your dress going to look like for this night of nights?'

'It's a long black evening dress with silver trimming down the split sides. Further, the silver trimming comes around to form a plunging neck line and down around my boobs.'

'My God, that really sounds very sexy.'

'You will see just how sexy it really is tomorrow night.'

'On second thought, maybe I had just better stay home as this may just develop into a sex orgy and we'll all be declared *persona non grata.*'

'I've gotta run now, but I'll stop by on my way to Madam Nur's tomorrow night and pick you both up. What do you say, around 7.30 pm?'

'Great.'

'Hi Carlo,' was my greeting from Armando, as he opened the front door.'

'Elaine is just about ready as she is getting her evening bag or some such thing ladies get.'

'Wow, hello Miss Waterbury, Connecticut.'

'Come on now Carl, stop that.'

'Elaine, your dress is going to be the talk of the evening, I kid you not. Further, I can truthfully say you fill it out in all the right places. If you don't mind me telling you so, but I do think that the dressmaker could have used a little more material around the boob area. She didn't run out of material did she?'

'Carlo, is my hair okay?'

'Yes Armando, your hair is combed just beautifully I'll let you in on a little secret. If you want to get Armando out of your way for about ten minutes, just tell him his hair needs combing.'

'Good evening Count and Contessa De Cario,' with an attempted kiss on each cheek. 'Madam Nur, your Ambassadress, this is Carl.'

'Your Ambassadress, I'm most pleased to meet you.'

'Please come in and meet some of the other guests that have arrived. This is my dear friend Mr Osman Bey. Osman Bey currently serves in Adaman Menderes government. Mr Menderes is the Prime Minister of Turkey.

'Oh yes, I have heard the name. I'm very pleased to meet you Osman Bey.'

'This is the Ambassador to Brazil Mr . . .' she threw the name but it went right on by me.

'Very pleased to meet you your Excellency.'

'Nice meeting you Mr Crocker, and we shall speak later.'

'Thank you your Excellency, it will be my pleasure.'

'Armando, Mr Crocker seems to handle himself with ease and grace when meeting all these important persons.'

'Madam Nur, Mr Crocker can take care of himself as he comes from good stock and a good family.'

'Yes, Armando, I can see that.'

'Elaine darling, your evening dress is just stunning. Where on earth did you find it?'

'Madam Nur, darling, I didn't just find it, I had it specially made for your dinner party. The woman that made it is just fabulous. She has my measurements, and when I require something special, I just give her a call, plus give her an idea of what I desire, she just runs one up for me.'

'You mean, you don't have a personal dressmaker?' If you desire my dear, I can give you her name and telephone number. All very simple my darling.'

'Darling, aren't you a little apprehensive with the design of the dress at your top?'

'Not at all darling. When you have something like I have, that fills the top part of the dress, you just don't have a worry in the world about things like that.'

'By the way, I have a very nice couple who have just arrived here in Ankara. They have been married just a short time, so I invited them along. Elaine darling, they will be seated with you and Mr Carl at table No.9.'

'That will be nice. By the way Madam Nur, don't you think that is a stunning creation that the young lady is wearing?'

'Oh, that is Mrs Koç and she will be seated at your table with her husband. I must ask her if she had that that creation made here in Ankara or in Istanbul!'

'I'm quite sure it was fashioned and made in Istanbul by the looks of style and material.'

'I'll ask her later.'

'Elaine, may I have your drink freshened up a bit?'

'Thanks Carl, I sure need something after my last catty conversation with you know who.'

'All very understandable.'

'Mr Crocker!'

'Yes Your Excellency.'

'Isn't this a lovely dinner party Madam Nur is having?'

'Yes Your Excellency.'

'Tell me Mr Crocker, how long have you been in Turkey?'

'My first assignment or my second assignment?'

'Oh you have been here before?'

'Yes, I first came here to Turkey in the year of 1956 and was sent out to the Russian border.'

'That must have been very cold out there.'

'Cold is not the word for it your Excellency. If I were someplace else, I would say that it was cold enough to freeze the balls off a brass monkey, but I'm not someplace else.'

'I have gotten the message Mr Crocker. Mr Crocker, I have a rather important question that has been on my mind for a number of years. I'm sure you can answer my question for me without any problem.'

'I'll do my best, what is your question?'

'For a number of years, the United States Government has been giving millions of dollars in economic and military aid to Greece, Turkey, Spain and to Israel plus a few other countries, but has not given too much to my country, Brazil. Could you possibly explain why Carl?'

Oh shit, he has gotten me between the rock and the hard place. Standing there with two drinks in my hand, I'm looking around to see if someone, anyone could come running to my aid. I have just been asked a very powerful loaded question which has placed me in a very awkward and serious position. Looking quickly around I can see that I have caught Elaine's eye, but Madam Nur isn't about to let her slip away. I look hard and long at Elaine and my glances say . . . Help, I'm in trouble.

'Mr Crocker, I'm waiting for an answer.'

'Your Excellency, in the course of world and human events, we often times overlook that which is closest and dearest to us.'

'Oh there you are Carl. I was wondering where you had gone with my drink?'

'I thought perhaps you had gotten lost.'

'Excuse me Your Excellency, I have someone I want Mr Crocker to meet.'

'Thank God Elaine, you arrived just in the nick of time. In another couple of minutes the Brazilian Ambassador would have been asking more serious questions. However, he could not fault the answer I gave him, but next time I'll refer him to the American Ambassador. Better yet, to the United States State Department.'

'I see that Madam Nur has turned her living room into a huge dining room to accommodate her forty guests.'

'You could have fooled the hell out of me Elaine, as I've never been here before. I see she seems to have a lot of time for Osman Bey, but I'm sure it's business.'

'Yea Carlo, monkey business.'

'Armando, with the political situation like it is here in Ankara at the present time, a remark like that could land you in the land of the missing without explanation.'

'Unfortunately Carlo, you are very correct. I was speaking to the Mexican Ambassador just the other day and he was telling me that in some circles, diplomatic of course, that there are serious fears that there could be a revolution or a military take over of some kind. Needless to say, things are not too good at the present time.'

'I don't know about you Armando, but I'm wondering when someone is going to sit their glass down and ring the chow bell? I'm getting hungry around the edges.'

Would you believe that someone must be reading my mind as they have just announced that we should go to our appointed tables. Oh yes, No.9.

'I'll hold your chair for you Elaine.'

'Thank you very much Carl. Carl, I don't believe you have met Rahmi and Mrs Koç.'

'I'm very pleased to meet you.'

'How long have you been in Turkey Carl?'

'Rahmi, may I call you Rahmi?'

'Most assuredly.'

'Well, this is my second assignment to Turkey. My first assignment was back in 1956.'

'Can you see much of a change in the time you were out of Turkey?'

'As a matter of fact, back in 1956 there were only 23 enlisted military personnel assigned to JAMMAT. Maybe, there were about twice as many officers, but they were out in the field. In short, back in 1956, there wasn't much of anything here in Ankara.'

'However, when I returned this time, they had changed the name of the headquarters to Joint United States Military Mission Aid Turkey. After that, they brought in the United States Air Force and thousands of US Military personnel. As far as I can see, that was a very big mistake. TUSLOG Detachment 30 grew and became a huge non-essential pain in the rectum. I believe in keeping such activities small, uncomplicated and functional. As the old story goes, we thought it was just great when Washington threw a dollar across the Potomac. Then came Truman who threw billions across the Atlantic. Will the brains of Washington DC never learn?'

'Please excuse me for saying what I did, but the people in Washington keep bringing so many young people into other countries and the young people just don't understand that they are guests in the countries they have been brought to and feel that they can act like they do when they are in their own country. That just isn't so as we all know. Traditions and customs must be taught and respected or otherwise we are breeding contempt, distrust and in general trouble. Now Rahmi, do you agree with me or am I just whistling a lot of hot air?'

96

'To the contrary, those are excellent words of wisdom. What do you think Elaine? You have been in Turkey longer than I have.'

'Truer words were never spoken.'

'Now that I have gotten that off my chest, what type of work do you do Rahmi?'

'Carl, I work with my family in our business.'

'I guess that gets a little exciting at times, doesn't it?'

'Ah, you may just say that.' From under the table, I just felt a slight kick on my ankle and it came from Elaine. I just got the message that I shouldn't persist on that line of questioning, but rather just drop the subject.'

'How long have you been married?'

'It's been about two months now, right dear?'

'Yes, about two months.'

'Since you are both new to Ankara and should you require any help regardless of what it may be, please feel very free to ask me. Do you have a pen Elaine?'

'Yes.'

'Thank you. Rahmi, this is my office phone number, so if you need any help, just call me.'

'Thank you very much Carl, I appreciate this more than you know.'

'Rahmi, I wouldn't say it if I didn't mean it.'

'Carl, I feel very sure of that.'

'Here you are Carl, this is my new office phone number here in Ankara. I too say, if you need help from me, day or night, just call this number.'

'Rahmi, I thank you very much, and I appreciate it.'

Here comes the first course. It looks like pumpkin Vichysoisse soup and you know what? It tastes like it. I'm told for the main course that we are having fillet of beef Wellington plus all the side dishes, topped off with strawberry cream freeze. 'What did you say Elaine?'

'I said don't eat too much as I'm told that you are going to have to sing for this group.'

'What did I tell you yesterday? I asked why I was invited to this dinner party as I somehow knew that I would be asked to sing for my supper. Do you remember?'

'Yes. Don't worry Carl, Madam Nur didn't forget to invite a very talented piano player from one of the top night clubs in downtown Ankara.'

'Yes Rahmi, after a fashion I do sing a little bit.'

'He sings very well.'

'Thank you Elaine, but you are being prejudiced.'

'No, just expressing my true thoughts.'

It was a very beautiful dinner and very nicely served. The dishes have all been cleared away and it seems like we are all waiting for show time. I can say, some more than others.

I see that Madam Nur is speaking to a man over by the piano. 'Ladies and Gentlemen, we are now going to enter into the fun time of the party. My very very dear friend Mr Halit will start off the evening's programme with a few selections on the baby grand piano just to get things moving.'

'What is that he's playing Carl?'

'Rahmi, that is called *One Alone* and it's from the Desert Song, by Sigmund Romberg.

'He plays very nicely.'

After a few more selections, Madam Nur addresses us once again and states that she would like to hear a selection from Mr Carl. I look at Mr and Mrs Koç and Elaine and they are applauding so I guess I had better make my move. As I reach the piano, I ask Mr Halit if he knows the *Birth Of The Blues*?

'That's one of my favourites,' as he ran his hands over the keys.

'Here goes. *And from the breeze in the trees singing sweet melodies . . . and they made that a part of the blues. And from the jail . . . the birth of the blues.'* Thank you very much it's very nice of you.'

'One more, just one more.'

'Mr Halit, do you know *April Showers*?'

'Okay.'

'*When April Showers may come your way, they bring the flowers that bloom in May . . . So keep on looking for the Bluebird and listen for his song . . . whenever April Showers come along.'*

'Beautiful, just beautiful.'

'Thank you all. Thank you Mr and Mrs Koç and Contessa De Cario. Thank you Mr Halit, it was very nice of you to play for me. Thank you again.'

'One evening Mr Carl, you are going to have to come to our night club and sing for us.'

'Thank you, but I'll have to think about it.'

'I'm not joking Mr Carl, you name the day and we'll make the time and we'll even put it in the newspaper.'

'I'm sure Uncle Sam would like to know that I have a second job on the side. I think that they call it *moonlighting*.'

'What is that?'

'I'm just joking. Again, many thanks.'

I hate to be a party pooper, but I believe it is time I take my leave before the Brazilian Ambassador tries to run me down again.'

'Yes, it's time that we also take our leave. Mr and Mrs Koç it has been a pleasure meeting you. Remember if there is anything I can do for you, please give me a call.'

'Many thanks Carl.'

'Madam Nur, your party was just excellent and I thank you for inviting me.'

'Thank you for entertaining my guests. You were just wonderful.'

'Thank you and good night.'

For the return engagement, I decided to have a few people in for a light buffet and cocktails. The guest list included the Count and Contessa De Cario, Madam Nur, whose husband had returned to his post in Ghana, Osman Bey, Rahmi Koç whose wife had returned to Istanbul, Master Sergeant and Mrs Lundy. Oh yes, Madam Nur's very dear friend who had just arrived from Istanbul was also invited. She was to stay with Madam Nur for about two weeks. All who were invited showed up on time. It was a very nice gathering with just light conversation. No, I didn't invite the Brazilian Ambassador as he asked too many strange questions. Everyone seemed to enjoy themselves and the food that I prepared. In spite of all the niceties, one could hardly miss the feeling or the under-current of the political situation which is now touching all of us. We knew things were happening in the government but we didn't know when or where. Osman Bey, being a Member of the Turkish Parliament and one of the right-hand men of the Prime Minister Adnan Menderes, seemed most vulnerable to any political comments uttered. For the most part, the afternoon went very well. The stereo played and some of the guests even danced. In some ways it reminded me of the *Titanic*. People were dancing the music playing, you knew the ship of state was sinking but you didn't know just when. In the Parliament, Menderes was coning under more fire with greater problems being raised than being solved. After about six hours, the guests started to leave. They all expressed their thanks for a very carefree and relaxed afternoon of eating and socialising. In short, it was just plain fun. When leaving, Rahmi Koç said that he completely enjoyed himself and hoped we could all do it again sometime. I didn't learn until later that after I had given Mr Rahmi Koç my telephone number and told him to call me any time if he needed help that I found out that he and his family were the richest people in all of Turkey. I felt that I had made a fool of myself and that they must have been laughing at me in private. However, I was most sincere.

By the end of March and the beginning of April, things politically were starting to hot up with the daily life in Ankara becoming a little more difficult. Newspapers which printed stories not consistent with the government or the political line, found their newspaper out of business.

It was during the latter part of April when I was returning from the open market place with my weekly supply of vegetables, when I was caught up in a political up-rising at Kizilay. I was knocked to the pavement by the running mob, lost some of my vegetables, got knocked down again when I tried to get up. I was finally dragged to safety by a quick-thinking Turkish Major. It all happened so quickly. One minute you are crossing the street and the next minute you are lying in the middle of that same street face down and the breath knocked out of you. Your first thought is that this could never happen to you and in fact that this is really not happening to you. But there you are, lying in the middle of the street wondering just how this did happen to you. 'Are you hurt?' the Turkish officer asked me.

'I don't think so,' I replied. It became very obvious that the mob didn't want anything to do with the Turkish Military as he helped me to my feet. He got me to the sidewalk and into the Berakan Hotel where he sat me down. I must have gotten hit with a flying stone or stick as I had a slight cut on my forehead. A young Turkish hotel waiter brought a cloth and washed the blood from my face. Thank God, it was only a superficial cut, but that was bad enough. Shortly, the Turkish officer introduced himself as Major Ibrahim. He spoke excellent English which surprised me. I asked him where he learned English and he stated here at the Language School in Ankara. When he passed his tests he was sent to the University of Texas for further studies. He ordered Turkish tea while I was trying to pull myself together after my unexpected ordeal. I noticed my bag of onions lying out in the street where I fell, but I sure in hell wasn't going out to retrieve them. After a short while the Military Police had the situation well in hand so I decided to head up the back street and make my way home. I thanked Major Ibrahim for his help and made my way home.

100

By the end of April, curfews were imposed on all sections of the country. In Ankara, military patrols roamed the streets and security check points were set up. More newspapers were closed. A feeling of uncertainty filtered through the population and even to the military. By the end of May, the government and the military seemed further apart with each passing day. On the evening of 26 May 1960, it must have been around midnight, small arms firing could be heard around the general area where I lived. On the morning of 27 May 1960, I was up early as I had an early work day. It was unusual, but my drivers hadn't arrived, so I started up my street heading for Atatürk Boulevarde and JUSMMAT. As I reached Atatütk Boulevarde, I'm greeted by a Turkish soldier who tells me 'go back to your home'. I'm in my US military uniform, but that seems to count for very little. I tell the soldier, I'm going to work at JUSMMAT Headquarters, and start to cross the street. Pointing his rifle at my head he tells me once more to go home. Needless to say, I didn't have to be told the third time. Returning home I learned from Radio Ankara that martial law was proclaimed. No one was permitted on the streets and we were to remain in our homes until further notice. However, this morning when I was up on Atatürk Boulevard I did notice that most of the Russian personnel in their Embassy were on their large balcony and had their electronic equipment working full bore. I'm sure that most Embassies were working overtime but from my vantage point I had full view of the Russian Embassy. The coup had been set in motion by the junta claiming action in defence of the Kemalist revolution under the leadership of Cemal Gürsel who was the former Commander of Land Forces of the Turkish Army. In short, the military under the command of General Cemal Gürsel had taken over the government and the country. Prime Minister, Adnan Menderes, now deposed was taken to the Island of Yassiada in the Sea of Marmara just off the coast of Istanbul. On any given day prior to the execution of Menderes you could see the Turkish warships on their 24 hour a day patrol around the Island of Yassiada. I don't know for sure, but I'm told that Osman Bey was also taken away. If that be the case, that would explain why I've had so many Eskiçis knocking at my door. An Eskiçi is a second hand dealer who deals in old and used goods. In my situation since I had Osman Bey here in my home, I think these Eskiçis are first hand dealers in Secret Police work. Be that as it may, I could have never proved it, but I would say that 16 Eskiçis in one week coming to my front door was a bit excessive in anyone's language. After the execution of Adnan Menderes in July 1961, for the next three years I never saw another Eskiçi at my front door. One could say, I must have passed their deep investigation or else I would have been bundled off to the local slammer for sure.

With more and more of my time taken up with my new military duties, I regrettably lost track of many of my dear Turkish friends. This is a situation I have always regretted. The words of Samuel Johnson still ring very true today when he said, 'Sir, a man must keep his friendship in constant repair or sir, a man will soon find himself left alone.' Sound advice.

With the days and weeks drifting by, I found that I had less and less time to care for my apartment let alone do my own washing and grocery shopping. As luck would have it, I met Mrs Backhouse at the Commissary while she was shopping and related my plight to her. 'Well Sergeant Crocker,' she said, 'maybe, just maybe I can help you out of your situation. If I can, I'll see you on Saturday morning at your place.' When Saturday morning arrived I had made up my mind that today was the day that I was really going to tear the place apart and clean it from top to bottom. Since I didn't have a washing machine, I put the bed linen and my soiled clothing to soak overnight in the bath tub. Needless to say I was really getting on with the programme. About 9.30 am my door bell rang. When I opened the door, there stood Mrs Backhouse with another older lady. 'Come in, come in.'

'Carl, may I introduce Hanna.'

'Pleased to meet you Hanna.'

'Hanna is here to take care of your place while we go out shopping.'

'Let me get changed and I'll be right with you. Hanna, whatever you need so far as cleaning material is concerned, you'll find it either in the bathroom or in the kitchen.'

As the weeks faded into months, Hanna became a very intricate part of my life. Let me put it another way. I lived there, paid the bills, but Hanna ran the house and me. It was all very mutual and things worked just like clockwork.

Chapter Five

There was a slight feeling of Spring in the afternoon air as I made my way back to JUSMMAT Headquarters after a trip to Etĭmesğut Airstrip. When I entered my office, Mrs Dençir, one of the office workers was in the process of answering the telephone in Turkish which was a little unusual for my office, but most acceptable. 'Evet Bey Effendi . . . Evet Bey Effendi,' she answered. I could see that she was a little excited and appeared on the nervous side with whoever she was speaking to. Under normal circumstances she always remained cool and unshakable. She put the phone down and appeared to have a stunned and shocked look on her face. 'Hi Mrs "D",' I said as she turned around.'

'Oh Carlcigim, that call was for you and they want you to be at the Turkish Parliament House tomorrow at 1400 hours sharp.'

'Slow down Mrs "D", who wants me at the Turkish Parliament House tomorrow at 1400 hours?'

'On the telephone was the Turkish Minister for Cultural Affairs and the Minister of Education.'

'Did they tell you what they wanted of me?'

'No Carlcigim, only that they wanted you there at 1400 hours sharp.'

My God, what have I done to deserve all of this? I know that I deal with the Minister of Customs and Monopoly for the importations and exportations of Military Household Goods and POVs (Privately Owned Vehicles). Maybe Chaplain Wilson's music that he has ordered for my Protestant Chapel Choir has gotten into the wrong channel and they want to turn it over to me. That must be it. Before I go home, I guess I should report this to the Secretary Mrs Joyce Backhouse so she can make a record of it just in case I should come up missing tomorrow afternoon.

'Hi Joyce.'

'What brings you up here this afternoon?'

'Mrs "D" in my office received a phone call from the Turkish Ministry that I should report there tomorrow afternoon at 1400 hours sharp. Needless to say, you can never be too careful when you are in a foreign country.'

'How true.'

'No, Joyce, they didn't tell Mrs "D" what they wanted of me, only to be there at 1400 hours.'

'Thanks Carl, I will inform the General upon his arrival back in to the headquarters. I'm sure that he will be interested as to what transpires.'

'That will make two of us.'

'Thanks, I'll see ya later.'

As I left JUSMMAT Headquarters I walked slowly up Atatürk Boulevard towards the Russian Embassy and across the street to Gülözü Sokak. Walking down the street, the Contessa De Cario is on her balcony and motions for me to come over. Worried about the phone call and what is in store for me tomorrow, I really don't feel like too much conversation.

'Come on up Carl, and we'll have a short drink as Count De Cario, is home from the office. What's the matter Carl, you look like you have just lost your very best friend?'

'Not really Elaine, but I had a rather disquieting phone call from the Turkish Ministry today. The Minister called my office but didn't tell Mrs Dençir what they wanted of me at the Ministry tomorrow. For all I know, they may declare me persona non grata for the last concert which was held in the Government Concert Solunu two months ago. As I remember, the music presented by the choir was just beautiful. Maybe, because it was Christian music and not being Muslim music, they took offence.'

'I just don't know at this point what to think. Oh shit, there is just no sense sitting here worrying about it. Armando, I'll have another drink if I may and then head home.'

'Sure Carlo.'

'Did I tell you that I saw Hanna at the shop today when I was there? I think that she was getting some tender bone fillet from the butcher and she was making darn sure that it was tender.'

'Elaine, for a woman who is 68 years old, about 5 feet 3 inches tall and weighing about 135 pounds, she sure keeps going and keeps me on the hop as well. Frankly, I've never seen anything like her and perhaps never again. Just this morning she arrived at 6.05 am and caught me in my underpants and T-shirt having a cup of coffee. When I asked her why she was here so early, she told me she had gotten a ride in the very big black car with her friend Ismail.'

'He is my good friend.'

'What you have to know Elaine is that her friend Ismail is the chauffeur for the President of Turkey. In short, she was driven here to my place to work in the presidential limousine. She then quickly added that she had kept her head down all the way here. Elaine, Hanna wouldn't know a private from a President and that's what makes her the sweet and wonderful person she is.'

'What was that Armando?'

'I said, maybe that's the reason they want to see you at the Ministry tomorrow about Hanna. You know in this area with the Russian Embassy, Brazilian Embassy, Austrian Embassy, Mexican Embassy and the Dutch Embassy and are just crawling with secret police who are acting like street sweepers.'

'Maybe, just maybe one of them saw her get out of the limousine.'

'Who knows, maybe they did. However, that thought had passed my mind.'

'You know, speaking about Hanna brings to mind how she came to be here in Ankara and Turkey in general. As a young girl, so she related to me, she was born in Budapest, Hungary. She was quick to relate that she was raised in Little Pest which is just across the Danube River from Budapest and not to get it mixed up. Frankly, I wouldn't know the difference, but it seemed most important to her. Anyway, as a young girl she saw this very handsome young man one day while she was out shopping for her mother. "You must remember," she continued, "I hated shopping of any kind. When I saw this man I just couldn't take my eyes off of him and I even followed him across the river to Budapest." While relating this story to me she said, *Mösyöciğim* my heart did a flop flip and I knew that he was the man for me. As I followed him, I saw that he had gone into the Turkish Embassy and I didn't understand what he was.'

'What d you mean Hanna?'

'Well *Mösyöciğim* why would a Hungarian man go into the Turkish Embassy unless it was for something not so good?'

'I don't know Hanna, you tell me?'

'At this point, my mother just couldn't understand why I suddenly took so much interest in going to shopping when before I hated even the mention of the word. Of course, I didn't tell her about this man I saw and how I was following him. Should I have mentioned it to Mama, she would have put a stop to it at once besides telling Papa. I just made up a little story as to how I was finding shopping interesting for the first time. Further, meeting new people while shopping and to, what you say, haggle over the prices. As far as I know, Mama never said anything or told Papa, but somehow I think she understood something was wrong in Little Pest by my actions.

Winter has now left Budapest and the spring rains have taken over bringing all the beautiful flowers to life once again on both sides of the Danube River. The love that I have built up in my mind for this young handsome man didn't melt away with the winter snows. In the back of my mind I just knew that I had to devise a way to meet this man and to speak with him. I just couldn't keep going on this way as I was beginning to have sleepless nights with strange feelings bubbling to the surface inside of me. I had never felt like that before.

About two weeks later when I was out shopping for Mama, she continued, quite by accident I hit a man with my long French stick bread on the head and knocked his hat off. I was embarrassed. When the man picked up his hat and turned around to me, I nearly died. it was him.'

'Don't stop there Hanna, tell me what you did.'

'*Mösyöciğim*, I just stood there and looked at him. All of the words and phrases I had in my mind before to speak to him, just didn't come out. I just stood there and looked at him and then he spoke.

'May I help you with your packages?' he asked.

'Would you be so kind,' I replied. I noticed an accent in his voice, but it was just beautiful. 'Do you live in Little Pest?' I asked.

'No, I live across the river in Budapest.' Not trying to appear too bold, or inquisitive, I asked him what kind of work he was into and if his wife liked his profession.

'I'm in the translation business, was his response. As to my wife, I really don't know as I'm not married. I'm currently working in the Turkish Embassy here translating old Turkish language into the modern Turkish language, which President Atatürk has introduced to us. Enough about me. What kind of work does your husband do for a living?'

106

'Husband? I have no husband, I live with Papa and Mama in Little Pest.'

'Do you work?'

'No, I help Mama around the house and do a lot of cooking for the family.'

'I bet you are a wonderful cook?'

'Oh not too bad, as we just have plain Hungarian cooking, as Papa just likes plain food.'

'By the way, what do I call this beautiful young woman before me?'

'Who, me?'

'Yes, you.'

'I'm Hanna and . . . and I must run now. Thank you for helping me with my packages,' as I jerk them out of his hand and run off.

That was close, I hope that Mama hasn't seen me talking to . . . to . . . oh my God, I didn't even ask him his name and now he is gone. 'Oh Hanna, there you are.'

'Yes Mama.'

'What has happened to the long French stick loaf of bread which is now not so long?'

'It was broken in the crowd when I knocked a man's hat off.'

'Very well, we'll get another one on the way home.'

Two days have passed and I haven't been able to see him near the shops. My heart seemed heavy and I was thinking that he had left Hungary and returned to Turkey. I went to the Turkish Embassy several times, but I couldn't make myself enter. Who was I going to ask for, as I didn't even know his name.

One Sunday afternoon Papa, Mama and I were out walking when I saw him coming our way. It was right there and then that I made a conclusion. 'Excuse me Hanna, don't you mean a decision?'

'Yes *Mösyöciğim*, I made a conclusion. I went up to him and asked him his name. He said his name was Ali Bey. I turned to Papa and said, 'Papa I want to introduce Ali Bey.' Papa in turn introduced Ali Bey to Mama. Both were very pleasant and I was praying for a miracle. I wanted Papa and Mama to like him but I didn't want to show them my feelings towards Ali Bey. Papa was very nice and Mama smiled. Looking at Mama, I had a strange feeling Mama's smile said more that what words could be said. I think she knew that I was deeply in love with Ali Bey and would have liked to have been alone with him, but that wasn't possible yet. The way Papa was asking Ali Bey so many questions I was beginning to have hot and cold flushes. The way Papa was carrying on I thought Papa was going to ask Ali Bey if he had seduced me. I broke into their conversation, 'Papa, Ali Bey must leave now to return to his office or he will be late. 'Ali Bey I'm sorry that I have detained you so long. Please come and visit with us sometime.'

'It was nice meeting you Ali Bey,' Papa said while Mama only smiled. As we continued our walk, Papa said that he would like to invite Ali Bey home one Sunday for dinner.

As the weeks and months passed, Ali Bey was at our home nearly every weekend he was free. One Sunday afternoon when Ali Bey came he brought flowers for Mama and some new blend of pipe tobacco for Papa. Of course he didn't forget me and gave me two nice lace hankies in a pretty little blue box. The conversation was light and happy until Ali Bey mustered up enough courage to ask Papa for my hand in marriage. Dead silence struck at that moment as our grandfather's clock struck 4.00 pm. A tingling feeling rushed through my entire being with every heart beat. First, I looked at Ali Bey and then Papa. Not a word was spoken between them as my fate and future lay in mid air. I looked at Papa and then Ali Bey, but not a sound was forthcoming. Finally Papa took a breath cleared his throat, smiled and granted Ali Bey my hand in marriage. At this point, Mama asked if we would all like some more tea. I said to myself, Mama, who in the hell wants tea at a time like this? With no response from the three of us, she gently placed the tea pot on the table and smiled.

'As time passed we were married. We remained in Little Pest where both Jana and Jon were born. Both Mama and Papa were very happy to have their grandchildren near them. Deep down, you could sense their feeling that one day they would have to give them up and this I knew would break their hearts. However, for the time being these feelings were suppressed and pushed into the background and we all made the best of what we had and the time we had.

'Sadly, all too soon, the day arrived when we received orders that we were going to have to return to Turkey. There was much planning and packing to be accomplished and ever so much sewing which had to be done. I was filled with excitement and with a new sense of adventures which were about to unfold. Both Papa and Mama tried to wear happy and bright faces but in their unguarded moments their true feelings could be read like a book. Suddenly, these happy feelings I had started to give way to more sober realities that I would be leaving my home and my loved ones and maybe I would never have the opportunity to ever see them again. At this point I realised that I was grown up and would have to face the realities of life and accept that which life was about to offer me.

Ali Bey has taken care of all our travel documents and passports and has even gotten the train tickets. Yes, there is much excitement and plenty of anticipation. The children and I seemed in a wonder world of that which was about to happen. The following Tuesday all was in order so we all, Papa, Mama, Ali Bey, Jon, Jana, and some of our friends all left for the main train station in Budapest. Laughing gave way to tears and they flowed down our cheeks like small tributaries into the Danube, ever so gentle. In the distance, Papa saw a man coming our way and he seemed to be in a very big hurry. 'Bey Effendi . . . Bey Effendi . . .' he shouted while waving a white paper in his hand. With the conversation being spoken in Turkish, it must be a man from the Turkish Embassy. During the brief time they had spoken, our travel plans changed dramatically and considerably. It seems that my husband Ali Bey has to return to the Embassy for a few more days and I am to take the children and proceed on to Turkey. Ali Bey will join me in Ankara. The train whistle was now blowing indicating that the few fleeing minutes we had together were fast slipping away. The sudden fear gripped my body and mind that I was soon to be left alone with only my children and heading into a completely new life and adventure without the security of my husband and my family.

I think that the full impact of this ordeal hit me when we arrived at Sirkeci Train Station in Istanbul on the European side of Turkey after a nerve racking trip across Europe. I suddenly realised that I only knew a few phrases in Turkish and they wouldn't even get me across the street should I have to use them. My God, my God, in what a hopeless situation I suddenly find myself. I'm trying to keep a brave face for the children's sake. Here we are, two young children in a strange country and I must find my way across the Bosphurus to Haydarphasa train station on the Asian side of Turkey and I don't even know which direction it is located. As I'm standing there, I can't help it, tears slowly started tumbling down my cheeks while the children were playing hide and seek around my dress and were oblivious to the situation surrounding us. Ali Bey, Ali Bey, where are you now that I need you so dearly? As I was fumbling for a hanky in my handbag, the young woman who was travelling in the same car on the train, came up to me and wanted to know if something was wrong. She spoke to me in Turkish and could quickly see that I didn't understand a word she was saying. Ah, she said and she spoke to me next in German. Out of sheer delight I grabbed her and hugged her which fully expressed my feelings of relief and gratitude. Once we had gotten our luggage out of Customs, she hailed a taxi which took us to the Galita Bridge where we boarded a boat for our trip across the Bosphurus to Haydarphasa Train Station. Selma, that was her name, and I reached the station with our luggage inspite of the crowd of people at Haydarphasa station going towards Asia. I watched the children and our luggage while Selma got my ticket to Ankara. Selma had no such problems as she was only going to the seaside town of Pendik which is only about an hour's ride from Haydarphasa station. When all was in readiness, we departed Istanbul and were heading for Ankara.'

'No thank you Armando, I really must go home and have my shower and get a bite to eat. Like I said, I have a pretty rough day ahead of me tomorrow.'

'What was that Elaine?'

'No water. Oh God, if you have gas and electric, you don't have water. If you have water and electric you don't have gas. It's been months since we have had all three at the same time. One day, when the population stops shifting, we may get back to normal and having water, gas and electric all at the same time.'

'True Armando, you save money by not having them, but really I don't mind paying so I can have my shower when I want to take it and not when the city fathers set their off beat time for various services to be on. Well kids, since I have such a long way to go, just across the street, I had better make my move so you people can get on with what you have planned.'

'Oh we are going to Armando's mother's place for a light evening snack so I don't have any cooking to do. Again, many thanks for the drinks and the conversation.'

It's just good to be at home again. Yep, we have lights, but for how long who knows. I had better make sure that Hanna has turned off the gas in the flash heater just in case the gas goes off during the night. Who in hell wants to be gassed to death in one's sleep. After my shower episode a few Sundays ago when the water went off when I was all soaped and standing in the shower, I now keep a large earthenware jar

110

in the bathroom to flush the toilet or to rinse me off should the case arise. Just keeping up with the various utilities activities here in Ankara is more than a full time job. Frankly, I don't see how the authorities manage.

Now to put some records on the stereo, eat my salad and Börek which Hanna made for me, and let life pass me by for a little while. Ah yes, Frank Chackfield's music seems to settle my jangled nerves when I'm all pooped out. Nothing like good music to settle a person down.

With my handy work check list, I see that I must meet the Erzurum train tomorrow morning at 9.00 am and pick up Colonel Barlow and get him settled into the Bulivar Hotel. He's in for the teams courier run. Knowing Colonel Barlow as I do, I know that he will want to do a lot of running around and will want me by his side to do his translating for him. He is one of the last big spenders. I had better take my dishes out to the kitchen as it is getting time when I should be pressing those sheets and getting into the prone position for a few hours sleep.

Morning arrives all too early and I feel as though I have just gotten into bed. However, regardless how I feel, I know I should make a move before you know who arrives and really starts my day off with a bang. That's one thing I really won't be requiring today. With what I'm faced with today, I can get by nicely without it.

Oh damn . . . the water is still off so there will be another day without my shower. My only hope is that my deodorant doesn't run out before the water is back on. This situation is enough to make a holy man take up drinking. Before my deodorant is applied the next best thing is to do what I call operation birdie bath. I'm beginning to wonder how the other half lives up in the President's Palace. Surely, they must be faced with the same problem as me? On the other hand, I guess the President must have his own private well with all the servants drawing water from it to satisfy all his needs. Wishful thinking won't get the job accomplished so I had better make tracks before Hanna arrives.

I have about thirty-five minutes before Hanna is due to pop through that door in all her innocent glory. I'll let you in on a little secret. That is, if you want to carry on a conversation with Hanna, you must have a working knowledge of Turkish, German, French, English and Pidgin English as well. It's not that she speaks all these languages fluently, but she mixes them all up to form a complete thought or sentence. You must keep on your toes at all times when speaking to her

111

or you will miss your cue word be it in German, French, Turkish, English, or Pidgin English or you may well miss the entire point of her conversation. Case in point. She will say, *'Mösyöciğim, var goenze simdi?* Now you take *Misure* (French) *cigim,* (Turkish) *var goenze* (German) *simdi?* (Turkish again)' When translated it means . . . Mister where are you going now? You can see, that even a simple conversation can become complicated and you haven't even started your day yet. With such daily brain stimulation who needs more mental stress which I'm about to face today. I'll just fix myself a cup of coffee and just relax a few minutes before Hanna comes bouncing through the front door. In all fairness I should tell you that Hanna does not like my landlord. She would tell you very quickly that he is a no-good man and she no likes him. For openers, he is a ruthless businessman who delights in taking advantage of people who he feels are less fortunate than himself. He tried his brand of crap on me, but found out only too quickly that I wouldn't put up with any of it. What happened was the light globes in the stairway were burnt out and he was so cheap he wouldn't replace them. Living on the fourth floor, it was rather dangerous going up the stairs with very little light. I took it upon myself to replace the light bulbs with the very same wattage as the ones I had taken out. However, three nights later the timing device burnt out and he came knocking on my door telling me that since I had put the new light bulbs in, that I had broken the timing device. Further, since I had broken the timing device I would have to buy a new one and have it installed. Anyone with an ounce of brains would know that was a bunch of hogwash, but he tried it on me. At the time he knocked on my door to tell me that I had broken his timer, I was in the kitchen fixing something to eat and had the butcher knife in my hand. Not thinking, I answered the door with the butcher knife still in my hand. In English he told me that since I had put new lights in the stairway, that I had broken the timer and I would have to pay for it. I told him that he was a fuck'en liar and to get out of my apartment. As he lowered his eyes, he saw that I was holding a butcher knife in my hand and not another word was spoken. He shot back across the hallway to his apartment, banged the door shut, and the subject of the timer was never raised again. The following day we had a new timer installed. One day when I finally told Hanna what had happened. She smiled and said, *'Mösyöciğim,* you no worry, I fix.' I smiled, and put the incident out of my mind.

As the days passed, I came home for lunch one afternoon only to find Hanna very happy and just beside herself.

'What's the matter Hanna?' I asked. She was half snickering and laughing and answered, 'Nothing *Mösyöciğim*.' Just the way she was carrying on I had a feeling that she had been up to no good, but that was Hanna. Sitting at the dining table having my lunch, I heard a God awful sound in the hallway and it sounded like my landlord. At this point I saw Hanna take her apron and put it up to her face. The apron helped muffle the laughing which had now become almost uncontrollable. The louder he yelled in the hallway, the louder and harder Hanna was laughing in the kitchen.

'*Mösyöciğim,*' she interjected, 'I think I made mistake in my panties,' as she continued to laugh. Between the landlord yelling and Hanna's laughing I heard him yell something like '*Allahin belasi kedi.*' Hanna only laughed louder. *Allahin belasi kedi* would translate into something like 'God Damn Cat.' Now I seem to have gotten some of the complete picture. In Turkey as in some other countries, the street shoes are removed prior to entering the home and left at the front door. As I see it, Hanna waited for him to come home for lunch just before I did, slipped out and put a few drops of water into each of his shoes, slipped back in to our apartment and closed the door. When the landlord got ready to go back to work, he went out slipped his feet into the shoes and put his feet into the water of each shoe. Thinking that the cats had been in the stairway he blamed them for pissing into his shoes. Hanna may have been old in years, but her mind and actions were those of a teenager.

As I'm leaving the apartment Hanna is coming up the stairs. 'Oh *Mösyöciğim*, you are little early bit going today.'

'Yes Hanna, Colonel Barlow is in from Erzurum on courier duty and I have to pick him up at the Bulivar Hotel this morning.'

'You little bit lunch eat today?'

'No Hanna, I have a very full schedule today, plus a meeting in the Parliament House.'

'*Mösyöciğim*, why you to go Meçlis?' Trying to be smart, I told her that I had to see a man about a horse. She looked at me and finally said, '*Mösyöciğim*, only the back side of horses are there.' I had no idea that she would ever understand or know that expression. 'Horses Asses.' Well, live and learn each day with Hanna as you never know what to expect, and I mean never.

When I arrive at the Bulivar Palas with my driver, Colonel Barlow was standing just inside the door waiting for our arrival. With a salute and a greeting, we were off like a group of tourists in our three-quarter truck heading for JUSMMAT. After making his official calls, which took about forty-five minutes, we were off to the 'Car Barn Area' to do the Commissary shopping, along with the Post Exchange and Class VI shopping. He dropped off his grocery lists at the Commissary and then went on to the Class VI to leave the liquor order there as well. Back to the Post Exchange he went. My driver and I went around to the Commissary to wait until their personnel had his order filled. As the boxes were filled they were placed in the back of the truck. After two trips back to JUSMMAT to put the groceries in my store room the Commissary shopping was completed. Now came the Class VI orders. Again I had to wait until the orders were filled and packed. From the looks of the two orders Commissary and Class VI I would estimate that about $2,500.00 had been spent. Now to find Colonel Barlow and get him and any other items he has purchased back to the JUSMMAT store room. From the looks of all the cases of liquor and wine that had been purchased they must be having a big drought up in Erzurum or expecting a lot of visitors. Being up in the general area where Noah's Ark came to rest on Mount Ararat, maybe they know something that we here in Ankara don't know. To be sure, it will be their heads that are aching and not mine. Having been there for my year, I really know how time can drag and a little boost is always welcome at the end of the day to keep things moving. Having deposited all of the day's shopping in our secure store room I dropped Colonel Barlow off at headquarters and had my driver drop me off at the Turkish Parliament Building. After that I had him return to JUSMMAT Headquarters to find Colonel Barlow and to take him wherever he wanted to go.

While standing at the front door of the Parliament House watching the Military Security Guards manoeuvre back and forth, I was growing more apprehensive by the second. I'm not at all sure that I want to keep this date, if you can call it a date when directed by the Minister of the current government to be present. Oh no, the man coming towards me looks like one of the Security Police.

'Merhaba' (Hello), 'Size yardim edebilirmiyim?' (Can I help you?)

'Evet effendim.' (Yes Sir) 'Kültür baskaliginin nerede oldugunu söylermisiniz? (Can you tell me where the Cultural Affairs Office is located?)

'Baken sizi bekli yormu?' (Is the Minister expecting you?)

'Evet, beni bekliyor.' (Yes, he is expecting me.)

'Lutfen burada bekleyiniz.' (Please wait here, I'll call him.)

'Ben bir telefon edecegim. Afedersiniz efendim, bir Amerikali Bas Çavus Baken beyle bir randevüsü oldugunu söyliyor onun ismi Crocker'dir.' (Excuse me miss, there is an American Petty Officer here, his name is Crocker and he is telling me the Minister is expecting him).

'Bir dakika, randevu saatine bakalim.' (Just a minute, let me look at the schedule).

'Ah, Evet, tam zamaninda. Saat ikide Lutfen ona ofisi gosteriniz.' (Aha . . . right on time, 2 o'clock, please show him to our office.'

'Tesekkürler.' (Thanks).

'Evet effendim bu uonden lutfen.' (Yes sir, this way please).

Now I find myself at the secretary's desk facing two huge doors reaching from the ceiling to the floor, which I assume open into the Minister's private office. The secretary eyes me from top to bottom and I have a rather strange feeling that in some way she has undressed me mentally and is enjoying every minute of it. When the little hand on the clock gets to '2' and the big hand gets to '12' she alights from her desk, opens one of the doors, goes in and disappears behind it. Of course she wouldn't open the door wide enough for me to have a peek in, but closed it very quickly. I was thinking, you little cheeky bitch. Shortly, she emerged from behind the huge door and motioned for me to enter. I nodded my head to her and entered.

As I entered the Minister's office, my eyes quickly surveyed the interior surroundings like a hidden camera out of control. The rug I'm standing on is an Isparta red runner rug leading from the doors and ends at the front of the Minister's desk. Behind the large oak desk highly shined, sits the Minister. Behind him and to his right is a large bust of Mustafa Kemal Atatürk sitting on a pedestal presiding and overseeing all proceedings taking place. To the left, behind the desk, is a large Turkish flag with gold trim along the edges. On the left side of the office there is a settee with a small glass coffee table in front.

Taking a step or two towards the Minister, he rises, smiles, and greets me in very fluent English.

'Welcome to my office Sergeant Crocker. I see you are here promptly at 1400 hours as requested. I like punctuality.' he said. I responded with a shy 'Thank you.' As the Minister moved from behind his desk towards me I noticed several things which were most striking about this man. For openers, the vast majority of Turks have black hair, dark brown eyes, and dark olive complexions. However, such was not the case with the Minister. Firstly he had, sandy blond hair, light olive complexion and blue or blue-green eyes. Most unusual. Further, he stood about six feet tall, good looking, and was wearing a blue grey suit.

When you think of it, the blue or blue-green eyes would not be too uncommon in the general area of Istanbul as of today, or Constantinople of yesteryear. During the Ottoman Empire from the 14th Century to the 19th Century the Ottoman Turks ruled over an empire much larger than the Roman Empire. Their empire extended from Europe to Africa and to Asia. This reign lasted for over 500 years. Now you can see how the races mixed and genetic structures were changed. Even today, it is not uncommon to see a 'red headed' Turk walking down the street in any of the cities or towns in Turkey.

As the Minister came close, he extended his arm and we shook hands.

'It's nice to see you once again,' was his comment. Once again, I thought to myself. I don't ever recall meeting or seeing this man before in my life so what is this once again business? He continued, 'I attended your concert in the Devilet Concert Salounu and was greatly impressed with the masterful way in which you directed your choral group. At all times you had them in the palm of your hands and they too enjoyed it. Further, the music you had selected was very pleasing to the ear. Please sit down and make yourself comfortable while we speak.

'An orderly enters the room and comes directly to the Minister. '*Çay, Kahve, Gazoz?*' the orderly asks the Minister. The Minister turns to me and I answered '*Çay Lutfen.*' (Tea please). The Minister looked at me and smiled. I'm sure he had a feeling that I knew more of the Turkish language than I had let on. However, that wasn't my prime concern at the time. Why was I here and what did this man want of me? As we sat there he looked at me while I gave him a glancing look. I had a funny feeling like I was going to be like the proverbial sacrificial lamb which was being led to the slaughter.

The door opens and it is the orderly bringing in our tea. From his tray he handed me my glass of tea on a glass saucer with two lumps of sugar and a tiny little spoon. Once in my hand, instantly and rhythmically, the glass of tea, the tiny spoon and the two lumps of sugar started to beat like a percussion instrument being played in a great concert hall. The only way to stop this sound was to set the glass of hot tea and saucer on the table and get my shaking hand off of it. The Minister

116

smiled as he could see that I was very nervous and who wouldn't be under the circumstances. Trying to wear a brave face, I still didn't have a clue as to why I was in his office. Setting his glass of tea down, he looked at me and smiled again. Softly he said, 'I guess you are wondering why I called you to the Parliament and to my office?'

I half-way smiled and said, 'Well sir, the thought had crossed my mind.'

'Since your concert was being held in our State Concert Hall, I contacted one of our special technicians and had him set up the equipment to record your concert just in case I couldn't attend. However, I was able to attend plus the fact that I have the tape of your concert which I have now played for my colleagues for a specific reason.' I laughed to myself. The special technician he mentioned was nothing less than a secret policeman assigned to the Concert Hall. I'm a hundred per cent sure that a complete dossier had been completed on me prior to the Minister requesting me to come to the Parliament. Most of this information could come from the Turkish General Staff which really ran the country with the armed forces. When I was assigned to Erzurum my assignment had to be approved by the Turkish General Staff as that area I was assigned to was a very sensitive military area which bordered next to Russia. This military zone or responsibility was assigned to the Third Turkish Army of which I was a part.

'My reasons are these,' he explained. 'Prior to being elected to the Turkish Parliament, I had always felt that our country had missed out on many opportunities to expand and grow in a musical sense, so to speak. Therefore after seeing you and your musical group, I played your concert tape to my colleagues and they agreed, that with your help, we can expand our musical interests. This week, I'll contact the President, as the Presidential Symphony Orchestra only plays by the consent and decree of the Turkish President. I'll speak with the powers to be and obtain the required decree for the orchestra to play.' Sitting on the settee, I just looked at him. What in hell are these good intentional intellectual people thinking of? I have never directed a Symphony Orchestra before in my life and I didn't feel like I wanted to start now this late in life to do so. The Minister looked at me and said, 'Don't say anything now, as I know you must be overwhelmed with this offer.' Shit, I said to myself, overwhelmed, I have nearly pooped in my pants and I'm petrified. I don't know why, but somehow I have a feeling that there is more to this offer than the Minister is telling me. I'll just play it cool, as time will tell, I said to myself.

In their eyes, they feel that they have just done me a very great favour by offering me the pride of the Turkish nation, The Turkish Presidential Symphony Orchestra to conduct all by myself. The truth of the matter is that I feel washed-out, rinsed-out, wrung-out and ready to be hung-out. Why in hell didn't they just declare me *persona-non-grata* and let it go at that, as it would have been more merciful and less painful.

After having that bombshell exploding in my face, my host decided that maybe he should let me go before I fell completely apart.

With a very firm handshake and a pat on the back, he walked me to the door. 'Thank you very much for your help in this important matter and I expect your answer by tomorrow before 1700 hours.' With that statement, the huge door opened and closed behind me.

SOP (Standard Operating Procedures) clearly state that under the circumstances I am bound to report such meetings to the American Ambassador at the Embassy of the United States of America. What kind of a mess have I gotten myself into now. From the Turkish Parliament Building near Kizilay, I can walk the four very long blocks to the American Embassy and make my report.

As I enter the main downstairs lobby, a Marine Sergeant in his dress blue uniform stops me and wants to know which department I wish to visit. I don't want to visit any department, but I have to see Bunny.

'Bunny,' says the Sergeant?

'Excuse me, I mean Ambassador Blair.'

'Do you have an appointment?'

'No.'

'I'm sorry Sergeant,' responded the Marine Sergeant, 'Ambassador only sees persons by appointment. You don't have an appointment so you have stated, but I suggest that you make one so he'll see you.'

'I haven't got time for such pussy-footing around. I just have to see him.'

'Sergeant,' he said to me again, 'since you do not have an appointment with Ambassador Blair, I highly suggest you take time to make arrangements to get an appointment.' This son-of-a-bitch is beginning to get under my skin and after what I have been through today it wouldn't take much to set off my fuse. It's damn sure I didn't come here to play Mickey Mouse games.

'Hi Carl, what brings you to the Embassy?' It's the Air Attaché

Colonel Dawson.

'Colonel Dawson, can we speak in private?' The Marine Sergeant gives me a rather dirty look for being able to get past him and into the Colonel's office. 'What's the problem Carl, you look very serious and a little upset.'

'What do you mean a little upset? I have spent the past two and a half hours in the Turkish Minister of Cultural Affairs Office in the Parliament upon his request.'

'What happened? Are you in trouble?'

'Trouble? That's not the half of it. I have to speak with the Ambassador and let him know what has transpired during my meeting with the Turkish Minister this afternoon. It's funny when you think of it.'

'What's that Carl?'

'The regulations specifically state what action I must take in such matters by reporting them but trying to fill this obligation is a different story.'

'Excuse me Carl, let me check with the Ambassador's Secretary, Miss Martin to see if he is too busy to see me now.' In an hour was Miss Martin's reply to Colonel Dawson's request.

'Carl, do you think that you can give me all of the important facts and details within the hour?'

'I'll do my best. The Turkish Minister and his other Ministerial colleagues have hatched up some fabulous idea that they want our church choir and their Turkish Presidential Symphony Orchestra to combine and present a complete programme using both groups. Further, they have insisted that I direct the whole shebang period. I was told that I had to give them a positive answer by 1700 hours tomorrow. Frankly Colonel Dawson, I don't want to do it, and that's final.'

'Carl, knowing these diplomatic and political situations we'll just have to wait and see what the Ambassador has to say on the subject. As you can see, this is a request from our host nation.'

'With all due respects to our host nation, I just don't want to do it.'

'Let's wait and see what the Ambassador has to say.'

In about thirty minutes Colonel Dawson's phone rang and it was the Ambassador's Secretary, Miss Martin asking Colonel Dawson to come to her office. 'It seems that the Ambassador will receive you, Colonel Dawson, in his office.'

'Thank you. Carl, wait here in my office and I'll return ASAP after speaking with Ambassador Blair.'

'Come in Dawson, what's on your mind?'

'I have a Sergeant Crocker downstairs in my office who has been contacted by the Turkish Government and has gone to the Turkish Parliament and had a meeting with one of the Ministers.'

'Crocker you say? Just a minute. Miss Martin, will go to my Top Secret File and bring in the file labelled *Operation Unsuspecting*. Thank you.'

'Here you are sir.'

'That's all Miss Martin. Dawson, you say contact has been made with Sergeant First Class Crocker, from JUSMMAT, who lives at Gülözü Sokak here in Kavaklidere?'

'Yes, Ambassador, but what is this all about?'

'Dawson, I believe the fewer people that know about this, the better.'

'Can I ask if he is in some kind of trouble?'

'I'll say no.'

'Excuse me Colonel. Miss Martin,'

'Yes sir.'

'Will you get Washington DC on the phone for me. I want to speak with the Secretary of State.'

'Good morning State Department may we be of help?'

'This is Ambassador Raymond Blair's office in Ankara, Turkey. Ambassador Blair wishes to speak with the Secretary of State concerning a very sensitive topic.'

'I'm sorry, but the Secretary has already left for the United Nations in New York. Is there anyone else here who may help you?'

'One moment please. Ambassador Blair, the Secretary is in New York at the present time, is there anyone else there who may help you?'

'Is the Assistant Secretary present? If so, I'll speak to him.'

'One minute please.'

'Hello. Hi Bill, this is Blair in Ankara.'

'Hi Ray, what's new in your part of the world?'

'Not too much, everything seems to be on the quiet side at the present time.'

'Since Dean is in New York today there seems to be a slight problem which he has the answer to.'

'What's that?'

'In his office, he should have a folder marked '*Operation Unsuspecting*. Further, by this time he should have marked in that folder if we proceed with the current plan or just drop it.'

'Just a minute Ray, I'll have my secretary Penny go and check with Joan, Dean's secretary, to see if they can come up with that folder.'

'One thing more Bill, the folder should be marked TS.'

'Okay. While she is getting it, what's new in your part of the world?'

'Well, the Syrians down in the Gaziantep area are making noises again, but the Turks have that situation well under control. The Kurdish people still want a state of their own out in the Diyarbakir region and are still fighting with the government troops. Other than that, things are buzzing right along.'

'Okay Ray, I now have the file marked *Operation Unsuspecting*. Yep, there is a note on the inside of the folder which states, should contact be made with a SFC Crocker by the Turkish Government, 'full speed ahead'. By the way, does this Sergeant Crocker have any knowledge of the contents of this folder?'

'None whatsoever Bill.'

'It states here the Crocker doesn't know the first thing about conducting an orchestra let alone a Symphony Orchestra.'

'One would imagine that this Sergeant is going to be in for one hell of a rough time.'

'That's the price a sacrificial lamb has to pay for someone at the very top screwing up.'

'You know Bill, that if he can't pull this off, some of his stripes will sort of come off in the process.'

'Bill, it's been very nice chatting with you, but I guess I had better get back to the business at hand here.'

'Take care, we'll be in touch.'

While sitting in Colonel Dawson's office on the main floor, the Marine Sergeant poked his head in several times and asked if everything was okay. I nodded, but frankly I'm sure he thought that I had other sinister motives so that's why he was keeping tabs on me. The last time he looked in on me he asked, 'Are you in some kind of trouble?'

I said, 'Yes, but it is far too complex, complicated and far too technical for you to understand.' He gave me one hell of a look and if looks could kill, I was a goner.

Shortly Colonel Dawson returned and stated that Ambassador Blair had placed a phone call to the State Department in Washington DC.

'Why in hell does the Ambassador have to call Washington DC and the State Department,' I asked.

'Well Carl, they are trying to contact the Secretary of State, to brief him on the situation here and to get his opinion on the subject.'

'Are you telling me that I have suddenly become a pawn in the international game? Colonel, I don't want any part of it, thank you.' Another hour passed and I'm getting rather tired of this entire affair. Besides, I'm getting hungry, tired and I have to pee. At this point the Marine Sergeant opened the door to Colonel Dawson's office and in came Ambassador Blair. I stood up as protocol dictates. Taking one quick glance at Ambassador Blair, it was easy to determine that he hadn't missed too many meals.

'Sergeant Crocker, I'll make this brief, (thank God I thought to myself, I have to pee) I have just gotten off the phone with the State Department and they highly suggest and request that you fill this obligation for the United States of America and the government of Turkey. I believe he called it 'Bettering Turkish and American relations.'

'Your Excellence, I protest, as I have never conducted a Symphony Orchestra in my life and never had the ambition to do so.'

'Sergeant Crocker, let me make myself very clear. Washington has spoken and it is my duty to ensure that their request is complied with, do I make myself clear?'

'Yes, sir.'

The Marine Sergeant smiled and showed me to the front door.

The son-of-a-bitches, I thought, they can sit in their plush offices and push us little people around to suit themselves. Should something go badly wrong with the programme, they say I have to do, who is going to get blamed, not them . . . me. By God, should this turn out to be a big success, they are sure in hell going to owe me and I won't let them forget it.

Saying good night, I slowly walked the one block from the Embassy to my apartment. I'm most distressed and disappointed with my fellow man and felt very downhearted about that which had just taken place. Surely, these people who live in their ivory palaces have little or no conception concerning the little guy or what he goes through. To them, only the final results count . . . regardless of how it is reached.

Placing the key into the lock of my front door, I really felt that I had been let down greatly by my fellow man who really didn't care about me but only their own egotistical ends. I really didn't know exactly how I was going to come to grips with the current dilemma which was forced upon me. As I closed the door, sat down with my face in my hands, all sorts of things went running through my head. God, I said, there must be an answer as I sure didn't have one. When you think of it, I thought, it's more than enough to make a preacher take up drinking. That's it! When I get to the office tomorrow I'll call Chaplain Wilson and dump this entire mess into his lap. Right now, I had better beat a path to the toilet and wee, as I'll soon have a mess to clean up if I don't. Feeling much better now so I had better see what Hanna has left for me in the fridge. Ah, look at that. Nice sliced chicken, salad, stuffed green peppers with rice, sliced tomatoes and some fresh baked Hungarian cookies. It all looks very nice, but I think I'll have a half of peanut butter sandwich with lettuce and a glass of milk and call it a night.It feels so damn good lying here in my little bed that I think I'll just stay here the rest of the day. On second thoughts, I had better get myself up, shave as it is nearing time for Hanna to come bouncing in. Yep, there is the key in the door which tells me that Hanna has arrived. In all good faith, I can tell you that Hanna is a very beautiful, warm and loving person, and looks over me like a guardian angel. Case in point. Just a few days ago 1st Lt Lori McBell, Nurse, United States Air Force, was leaving the following day for the States after completing her tour of duty here in Turkey. She came to say goodbye. When she rang the bell, Hanna answered the door. Opening the door Hanna said, 'What do you want?' Having not met her before Hanna wasn't letting anyone in to see me. While they were speaking I called out, 'Who is it Hanna?' She replied, 'It's a woman *Mösyöciğim.*' Hanna finally let her in as I was seated at the dining room table having my lunch. 'How are you Lori?' I asked.

'Fine,' she said. I'm leaving tomorrow and I just came by to say goodbye.' As best as I could figure out, Lori thought that Hanna wouldn't be here and we could really say goodbye. How wrong she was. Poor disappointed girl. Hanna was here and she wasn't having any part of it. To get past Hanna, would be like trying to get past the Rock of Gibraltar, impossible. Finally, Lori gave up and left with just a handshake while Hanna looked on and smiled.

As the front door opens, Hanna sings out, 'Good morning my *Mösyöciğim,*' which announces to the entire apartment building that she has just arrived. 'Oh *Mösyöciğim* you no finish making yourself pretty.'

'It's called shaving Hanna,'

'I know *Mösyöciğim*, Poppie does it also.'

'How is Poppie this morning when you came?'

'He is fine *Mösyöciğim*, but I think he is a dirty old man.'

'Hanna how can you say that about Poppie?'

'*Mösyöciğim*, I yesterday my house clean and I find some pictures of young girls and they have no clothes on. I asked Poppie when he came home what he was doing with these pictures and he no answer me.' I say again, 'Poppie vos is this?' He just look me *Mösyöciğim* and no say nothing.'

'Hanna, Poppie is 78 years old and I think that he can look at dirty pictures if he wants to.'

'No my house *Mösyöciğim*.' I say to him if he wants to look at dirty pictures to go to chicken house and not my house.'

'What did Poppie say Hanna?

'He made faces at me and told me to go milk a cow.' I laughed and said, 'silly old man, we do not have cow.' I looked at him and told him to go milk it. But I think that he was thinking of something else *Mösyöciğim*. Dirty old man.'

Now you can see how my day usually starts. Today I somehow have a feeling that we are about to start that game called twenty questions, a game in which Hanna is a past master.

'*Mösyöciğim*, you like I fix you to eat something?'

'No Hanna, I'll have a cookie or two and a cup of your good instant coffee.'

'Oh *Mösyöciğim*, you no big eat and I fixed nice and you no touch.'

'Maybe tonight I'll eat Hanna, as I got home late last night from the Amarikan Sefaret.' (American Embassy).

'Oh you went to party?'

'No Hanna, it was anything but a party.'

'You had good time *Mösyöciğim*?'

'No Hanna.'

'Why you go then *Mösyöciğim* if you no have good time?'

'Hanna, I must leave for JUSMMAT and see what Colonel Barlow wants to accomplish today.' As I make my move for the front door, I get my usual hug and a kiss plus a pat on the back. Now that I think about it, I have never figured out to this day what the pat on the back was really for. However, that was Hanna ever unpredictable, from one minute to the next.

As I walk up Gülözü Sokak to Atatürk Boulevarde, the Contessa De Cario is out walking her little dog Emir.

'Good morning Carl,' was her greeting. 'How did your meeting go with the Minister Yesterday?'

'Elaine, I really haven't got time at the present to tell you all of the happenings, but if you both are home this evening I'll stop by for a drink and fill you in.'

'Armando and I will be home waiting.'

'Thanks, I'll see you later.'

I cross Atatürk Boulevarde by the Russian Embassy. As usual, Uncle Joe Stalin's men are at the Embassy fence watching the street sweepers who are really Turkish Secret Police Force, and nobody is kidding no one. I usually see this same game played out each morning as I head for work. Needless to say, we have the cleanest street in all of Ankara. As I make my way towards JUSMMAT, I pass the new beautiful Parliament Building which is due to open later this year. It's a very huge and imposing building sitting on a slight hill which currently over looks the old Parliament Building several blocks away. The landscaping is all completed and the front lawn is a beautiful lush green. Turkish military currently occupy and guard the building to keep squatters and vandals out and away from the building. However, one of the most hilarious events I ever witnessed which was just last week occurred when a group of military personnel were trying to remove the old farmer's flock of sheep off the lush lawn of the Parliament grounds. There must have been at least 200 hundred head of sheep going in all directions munching on the lush grass. Traffic in both directions were blocked and more reinforcements were called into action. The farmer, who must have been 70 years old was just beside himself. The more the military personnel chased the sheep the more directions they would run in. Finally, a young soldier, who must have been a sheep herder prior to his induction into the Turkish Army got the old man and a bell and led the sheep off of the lush Parliament lawn. This only goes to prove once again that brains are much better than brawn.

When I reach JUSMMAT I see that my vehicle is parked in the lower level and my driver is in the vehicle. I check with my boss, JUSMMAT's Army Section, Adjutant General, who is by the way a relative of the Speaker of the House of Representative, in Washington DC. Even being a relative can't get me out of my current situation with the Turkish and American Governments. Seeing that the Adjutant had nothing special lined up for me, I guess I should hunt for Colonel Barlow who was last seen heading for the Snack Bar. Yep, there he is over in the corner having his morning cup of coffee and his donut.

'Good morning Sir, and how are you today?'

'Fine Carl, sit down and I'll get you a cup of coffee and we'll map our agenda for the day.

'May I have some sugar please?'

'Thank you.'

'By the way Carl, how did your meeting go yesterday at the Ministry?

'The meeting was fine, but the damn American Ambassador pissed me off. Colonel Barlow, please excuse my language, but those fuck'n bastards wouldn't listen to a word I was saying.'

'What was that?

'It seemed that all of a sudden everyone had hard of hearing problems and then they finally got lost in their own self importance and could care less that I was pleading with them to please listen to me. No, these ever loving public servants couldn't make a decision and called the State Department in Washington DC to do it for them.'

'What decision was that?'

'It seems that the Turkish Government wants my choral group and the Turkish Presidential Symphony Orchestra to get together and present a very big concert. However being honest, I told the American Ambassador that I had never directed a Symphony Orchestra before. I was told by the Ambassador to quit protesting and learn how to direct a Symphony Orchestra. I felt like telling him where to go and if he was so brilliant, why didn't he do it himself. Since it was after closing hours, I was shown out the front door and the matter was closed. Now you know just how I feel today.'

'I wish I could do something to help you but' . . . but as I interrupted by saying, 'yes Colonel we are in the same boat. It seems the Great White Father has spoken.'

'Are you finished here Colonel Barlow?'

'Yes Carl, I'll get my attaché case which I left in the Adjutants office and I'll join you here in your store room.'

'Okay.'

Opening the door to my store room it is easy to see that Colonel Barlow has been busy spending money for the team right left and centre. All of this will have to be repacked and placed into the heavy duty mail bags to be sure that they can endure the long trip back to Erzurum. Hopefully, they will arrive not bent or broken.

'What was that Colonel Barlow?' I said, since I have all of the team's shopping accomplished, I feel free to take my time and look around the old part of Ankara. 'Just as an interesting side note Colonel, did you know that the old part of Ankara was once the Citadel during the time of Christ and even before? There is sure a lot of ancient history surrounding the Citadel of modern Ankara which used to be called Galatia. Further, it is interesting to note that during this time the Galatians were not Muslim's as they are today. However, should you desire to broaden your knowledge on this subject, just turn to the Bible in the New Testament, to the Epistle of Paul the Apostle and his letters to the Galatians and you have it. I can say that it opened my eyes to this part of the world and the many wonders that have taken place here. Also, since I've been stationed here in Turkey, I have tried to learn the language and as much history about the country. As I see it Colonel Barlow, if you can learn and understand the history of a country, nine times out of ten you will have gained a much greater insight into the people, the country, and their interactions towards you. Case in point. Next month you'll be going to Southern Turkey for a NATO Conference. Right?'

'Right. Tell me, just what do you know about that particular part of Turkey and the surrounding cities of Samaria?'

'Frankly, nothing.'

'Today it would be called Izmir. Well, before, during and after Christ, Efus and Izmir were very major seaports on the Aegean Sea. During its hayday, Tarsus, another city in the south of Turkey played host to such notables and the mighty Queen of Egypt, Queen Cleopatra and the all powerful Roman General Mark Antony. As history tells us Queen Cleopatra needed the military services of Mark Antony's legions and his excellent knowledge of Rome and their battle strategies. History relates that she came calling to Tarsus with her royal barges in all their glittering glory. The display of grandeur even bedazzled the locals, but not least of all old Mark Antony baby himself. Once lured on to her barges with lustful advances and her sexuality and the events which followed, reminds me of a story about a little dog chasing a chariot down the cobblestone road in Tarsus. While the chariot was rushing down the road a little dog began running alongside of the chariot wagging his tail and barking at the wheel. Suddenly, the wheel ran over the little doggie's tail and cut it off. Feeling the sharp pain, the little doggie quickly turned his head around to see what had happened to his tail.

127

Ever so quickly, the wheel ran over the little doggie's head and lopped it off.'

'What happened then?'

'Nothing Colonel, but the moral of this story is, as Mark baby found out, was not to lose his head over a piece of tail. End of story.'

As you stand here and let your mind wander around in the walled city, you have the feeling that there is a story to be told on every cobblestone road within the Citadel. How many fights have taken place and just how many times has the Citadel come under attack and how many times have they been repulsed. To be sure, history abounds all around this place.

'Colonel, over here is one of the shops you may like to have a look. This is the same old rickety shop where I purchased my two silver and brass trays a couple of years ago. Needless to say, they won't come cheaply, but the workmanship is by far superior to some of the other shops.'

'I can see what you mean about the prices. The workmanship looks very good alright. This seems to be a good buy, don't you think? If you like it, I'll do the bartering for you.'

'It's okay with me.'

Carl. *'Effendim bu tepsi ne kadar?'* ('Sir how much is this tray?')

Shop keeper. *'Hangisi?'* ('Which one?')

Carl. *'Bu.'* ('This')

Shop keeper. *'Bu?'* ('This?')

Carl. 'Evet.' ('Yes')

Carl. *'Kaç Para Effendim?* ('How much money Sir?')

Shop keeper. '9,000.00 Turkish Lirasi.'

Carl. *'Çok Pahali.'* ('Too much money')

Shop keeper. *'Siz nekadar verir sinis?'* ('How much you pay?')

Carl. '7,000.00 *Lirasi* ('7,000.00 Lira')

Shop Keeper. *'Hayir effendim, çok az para.'* (No sir, yours is too little.')

Carl. *'Kac para, siz soyleyin?'* ('You tell me how much you want?')

Shop Keeper. '8,000.00 *Lirasi.'* ('8,000.00 Lira.')

Carl. *'Bir Dakiak Effendim, Bir Dakika.'* ('Just a minute Sir, just a minute.')

Carl. 'Colonel, he says he wants 8,000.00, no lower.'

Colonel. 'Carl, just how much money is that in US Dollars.'

'Colonel, that is $800.00 US dollars.'

'Do you think that is a fair price?'

'Colonel, under the circumstances and the workmanship, it seems to be a very fair price for this silver and brass tray.'

'Colonel. 'Okay Carl, tell him to wrap it up as I'll take it.'

Carl. *'Evet Alalim.'* ('Yes, we'll take it.')

Shop Keeper. *'Çok teşickür Ederim'* (Thank you very much.')

Carl. *'Esfullah.'* ('It's nothing.')

'Colonel Barlow, that wasn't too bad was it?'

'No Carl, not when you have someone like you to help me. It wasn't hard at all except maybe on my already depleted pocketbook.'

'Be that as it may Colonel, I really believe you got yourself a very good bargain. Is there any place else you desire to go Colonel Barlow?'

'I've spent most of my money so I guess I had better head back to JUSMMAT and take care of any team business there.'

'When we get back to JUSMMAT Colonel, I'll be in my store room getting all your items you have purchased packed and ready for shipment tomorrow. By the way Colonel, at what time do you desire to be picked up tomorrow and at which place?'

'Make it at 0930 hours and at my hotel. That should give me ample time all the way around.'

Now I had better go to my office and give Chaplain Wilson a call and let him know what has taken place at the Turkish Parliament and at the American Embassy yesterday. I'm sure he'll think that it's a big joke, but he'll change his tune when I bounce it off his balding head. Is he in for a big surprise. 'Chaplain's Office, Chaplain Wilson speaking.'

'Good afternoon good Chaplain, and how are things going today?'

'Oh that's you Carl.'

'Yes Sir.'

'Not too badly.'

'Do you want to bet Chaplain?'

'I don't understand what you mean Carl.'

'Well good Chaplain when I lay what I have to lay on you, you will undoubtedly blow a fuse which I've already done. I feel like I've been screwed by the fickle finger of fate and then dropped. I'll try to make the story very short and to the point. The day before yesterday when I returned to my office from Ettamgut Airstrip, Mrs Dençir had just received a telephone call from the Turkish Parliament which in a way concerned both of us. It was the Minister of Cultural Affairs arranging a

129

time and place for me to have a meeting with him concerning arrangements for a concert.'

'What concert are you speaking of Carl?'

'It's the one that some of the Turkish Ministers think that we should combine with the Turkish Presidential Symphony Orchestra and our Chapel Choir to present a big splash. That is the reason I had to go to the Turkish Parliament yesterday afternoon for the meeting at 1400 hours. After the meeting and knowing the SOP procedures, I had to go to the Embassy to report my contact with a foreign government official.'

'What did they have to say?'

'Let me say first, Chaplain, we have a problem.'

'Carl, we is plural.'

'Your English is so correct Chaplain, we have a problem.'

'What happened at the Embassy?'

'I first saw Colonel Dawson and he went to see Bunny.'

'Who?'

'Oh Ambassador Blair. He saw the Ambassador's Secretary who relayed his message onto the Ambassador. In a few minutes the Ambassador came out, got the complete story and went back into his office and called Washington DC.

'How did Washington DC get involved in this situation?'

'Hold on Chaplain, it gets better as it goes on. As I could best determine there seems to be a thing currently going on between Ankara and Washington and Washington wants relations with Turkey to improve. No reason given.'

'What happened next?'

'After a long wait, the Ambassador came out of his office and came down to Colonel Dawson's office where we were waiting. He stated that the State Department was most happy with the turn of events here in Turkey and that I would be most happy to oblige the Turkish Government with my presence. I told the Ambassador that I didn't feel qualified to take on such a responsibility. He turned to me and in so many words told me to shut my mouth as I didn't have any say in this political situation. I tried to explain to him that I had never conducted a Symphony Orchestra before let alone the Turkish Presidential Symphony Orchestra. He looked at me and said learn. Chaplain, I was so damn angry I nearly told the pompous bastard to do it himself if he thought that he was so brilliant. I didn't however, as it would have been my head that would have rolled. It only proves one thing and that is, you can't fight city hall, regardless of where it is located.'

'Carl, you must be upset, as I have never ever heard you speak like that before.'

'Upset? Chaplain, before this entire mess is over, you are going to hear a lot of things from me that you have never heard before. Trying to be a good Christian, and do the right things by all concerned, help your fellow man, and what happens? Someone will always turn around and try to screw you. Excuse me, Chaplain, but that is the fact of life. I'm tired of being screwed without being kissed.'

'Carl, you must be upset to use that terminology.'

'You can put it this way Chaplain. At the ripe old age of six years old, my father called us men and told us not to let other people force their will upon us. Further, to stand up for what you believe is right. With the passage of time Chaplain, I believe we have two impostors of right and wrong.'

'Which one is correct?'

'I don't know. Anyway Chaplain, I'll try to see you tomorrow after I get Colonel Barlow on the train back to Erzurum.'

'That'll be fine Carl, I'm most interested in your project.'

'Hold it Chaplain, it's our problem and our project.'

Oh damn it, I did promise to stop by to see Elaine and Armando so I had better get that out of the way, or Armando will never let me hear the end of it.

'Hi Elaine, I've just stopped by to have that drink you mentioned this morning. Where is Armando?'

'He's in combing his beautiful hair as usual.'

'You mean he found one hair out of place? I've forgotten what they call it, but it's like people washing their hands about twenty times a day.'

'What will you have?'

'The usual Elaine, bourbon and coke or whatever you have handy. I can't stay too long this evening, as I have a very busy day tomorrow getting my courier off to Erzurum. Briefly what happened at the Parliament House is that the Cultural Affairs Minister attended my concert at the Devilet Konser Salonu, the same one you attended and he liked it. Now he wants us to do a concert with their big Symphony Orchestra. I thought it was funny as I have never conducted a Symphony before. When I told the Ambassador he didn't think it was so funny and told me I had no choice and would do it. So, that's where it stands now.'

'Hi Carlo, I see that you could make it.'

'Yes Armando, I've made it and have been here for at least twenty minutes.' Whenever Armando calls me Carlo it means that he has been on the juice prior to getting home. 'I look at it this way Elaine. If I'm pushed into this situation and I hang, we're all going to hang.' I can see that Armando is about to fall asleep so I had better head home. 'I'll keep you posted with all the juicy intrigue. If there is any blood letting it will probably be mine, A RH Neg.'

Being a military man, I was well versed in the art of military operations, military strategy and even the art of killing. Political situations were left to the politicians who played with words and other governments. As an individual assigned my daily duties, I had little interest or no knowledge of that which was taking place on the world stage behind closed doors in Ankara, Washington DC, Athens and London. Some of the leading stars included; Lyndon B Johnson, President of the United States, Ismet Inönü, Prime Minister of the Republic of Turkey, Archbishop Markarios, President of Cyprus, Dr Fazil Küçük Turkish Cypriot Vice President, the British Government, the Greek Government with an added cast of over 600,000. I just wonder what Cecil B De Mille could have done with a situation like this. Regardless of just how small a part I was to play, and where I was to play it, it turned out to be the right part, the right time and the right place. Even Hollywood, if it tried, couldn't have come up with a better story line or epic to rival this plot. However, I was not informed and was oblivious to all of this which was seemingly ready to engulf me for the next three and a half months.

The morning started off with a bang as we had several good thunder storms. Currently, the skies look more promising and not as ominous as they were when I arrived at JUSSMAT. I see that my 3/4 ton truck is all loaded thanks to the Turkish Sergeant who sent me a couple of Askers (Turkish Soldiers). While I'm here and think of it, I should run up and see Joyce Backhouse and tell her what had taken place at the Parliament so she can relay that information on to the General.

'Good morning Joyce, and how are things here in the General's office today?'

'At the moment things are quiet, but I'm sure that will change quickly once the General gets in.'

'You can tell him that I got back safely from the Parliament and should he desire more information the Air Attaché at the Embassy can fill him in on all the details. When I see you later, I'll give you all the other details concerning yesterday's drama.'

'Oh that ought to be good,' she said, with a sparkling twinkling raised eyebrow.'

'To be sure,' I said as I left her office.

When we pull up in front of the Bulivar Palas Hotel, Colonel Barlow was ready and waiting and it wasn't even 0930 hours.

'Good morning Colonel.'

'Top of the morning to you Sergeant. I see you are prompt as usual and I have all of my belongings right here.'

'Okay Sir, I guess we are ready to head to the train station.'

Backing into the cargo section of the station, the baggage handlers, (Hamal), rush forward to greet us. Having been through this mess many times before, I now have it down to a science. I take out my little black book and start calling names. Turgut, Ismail, Recep and Mustafa. These are the four baggage handlers for today Colonel Barlow.'

'Sir, if I didn't you would have about twenty-five or thirty baggage handlers swarming all over you and you wouldn't know if your cargo had gotten on the train or not.'

'You mean you have them broken down in teams?'

'Spot on Colonel. This way, they know what team they belong to and respect each other's right to work the Erzurum Courier in proper shifts. No pain, no strain, and you pay only one handler and he divides the money up evenly between them. This morning with all the baggage we have, it will be about 300 TL. That's not bad at all.'

'Sergeant, I want to thank you for all of your help on this trip which made things a lot easier for me and your help in buying my tray.'

'Colonel Barlow, it was my pleasure. Have a good trip back and give my regards to the team members.' Slowly, the train starts to pull out of the Ankara station heading for Eastern Turkey, arriving there two and a half days later.

I should go and tell my boss what has been happening over the past 36 hours to keep him up-to-date. Needless to say, I will have to have a few hours off each day to get this concert off the ground and running.

'Sir, I have to inform you what has taken place concerning the Turkish Government and the US Government and me.'

'Sergeant Crocker, I was upstairs to the General's office and Mrs

Backhouse told me that the General had gotten a report from the Air Attaché concerning your activities.'

'That is what I wanted to talk to you about. Sir, I will require some time off from my work in the headquarters to work on that . . . Quote *Special Project* unquote, which the Ambassador said that I had to do.'

'Sergeant Crocker, your prime duty is required here in this headquarters and it is not possible to give you any additional time off for your *Special Project*.'

'Sir, I would like to point out that this is not my Special Project, but one that was dumped into my lap.'

'Let me put it this way Sergeant, it's your baby, so you will just have to live with it.'

'Sir, I do want to thank you for your kind understanding of my problem.'

He may be the relative of the Speaker of the House of Representatives, of the United States of America, oh shit, by saying it will only raise my blood pressure. I'll respect him only because he wears the US Uniform, but other than that he doesn't mean anything to me and that goes for his dog as well. Now what do I do now? I had better give the Chaplain a call to see if he is going to be home this evening so we can start making some plans and ordering the music.

'Hi Chaplain, will you be home this evening so we can start making some plans and to see which way we are going so far as this concert is concerned? Good, I'll see you about 1830 tonight. Thanks.'

'Hi Chaplain, I'm here to off load some of my problems on to your door step. This afternoon, I spoke to my boss the Adjutant General to see if I could get a little time off to get this special project off the ground, but he slammed the door in my face so to speak and told me it was my problem.'

'Do you want me to speak to him?'

'No Chaplain, I wouldn't give him the satisfaction to let him know that I even mentioned it to anyone.'

'No Carl, but he will be the one person that will be ready and willing to accept all the bows should this concert be a big success.'

'Chaplain, tell me about him. In my world travels I have seen them before and after, so what is new? To put it another way, those kinds of people are a dime a dozen but I came here to get something positive accomplished. As it stands now, I don't believe our forty voice chorus can hack it with a large orchestra. We will need approximately sixty or more voices to even make a dent in that orchestra. We'll just have to

134

make that our number one priority for starters. Further, since the bulk of the present chorus has done the *Messiah*, by George F Handel, it would be less work and give us a nucleus to work with. Doing it this way, I would only have to worry about the new members of the chorus learning their parts and would have the help of the old members. This would give me more time to learn how to conduct a Symphony Orchestra. Chaplain, you know as well as I do, that something with the magnitude of this special project requires a lot of time for planning, execution and cannot be accomplished with a snap of the fingers. I figure we will have about fourteen weekends plus any time that I can get the groups together for rehearsals. One big hurdle everyone has forgotten about is that the Symphony Orchestra personnel only speak Turkish and the Choral Group only speak English. Further, the Choral Group will be familiar with the music, if we choose Handel's *Messiah* and it will all be new to the orchestra. Further, I will have to learn all new Turkish musical terms, plus how to direct the Orchestra and the Choral Group all at the same time. You know the more I think about it, and the more I talk about it, the more it scares the piss out of me.'

Since my first meeting with the Chaplain, a lot of water has flowed under the bridge so to speak. The Minister has been informed as to the music we plan on doing and approved. Further, the music for the *Messiah* has been ordered for the Orchestra and the Choral Group plus the Conductor's Copy. New York has promised delivery in ten days. The wheels have been set in motion and now the real hard work is about to commence and already I'm beginning to feel the pressure building up. As the days and nights passed, time was becoming my staunchest enemy and there was nothing I could do to make it stop. During the evening hours I worked with the Choral Group and even had them broken down into sections of tenors, basses, sopranos and altos. When the music arrives for the orchestra, I will take an LP recording of the *Messiah* to the concert hall and will let them sit and listen to the music and try to let them hear the music as it would be supposed to sound when we start their rehearsals. Doing it this way I thought, they will at least have some concept of what it should sound like and not just cold Turkey. (Excuse the pun). I'm most happy as the chorus has built up to 85 people which far exceeds any of my expectations.

With the passage of days and weeks, there were rehearsals, rehearsals and more rehearsals. The day was fast approaching when I will be compelled to start putting the entire groups together. During the meantime, I have been working with my Concert Master whenever his time and my time would permit which sadly wasn't enough time to really learn how to conduct a symphony orchestra. From time to time, my boss, the Adjutant General of the Army Section would ask how the 'special project' was going with a slight laugh in his voice. Frankly, he really didn't care if the programme was progressing or not. I felt like saying something, but I would not lower myself to his standards.

I now have just four frantic weeks to put this disjointed programme together. I still haven't received my Conductor's Copy of the *Messiah*. We have placed an urgent call to New York City publishers and they tell us that it has been dispatched. Where in the hell is it?

I have borrowed another recording of the *Messiah* and I have started to commit both the orchestral and vocal parts we are doing to my memory. By God, this sure wasn't in the bargain and it is hell getting all my brain cells screwed up right left and centre. Now I'm forcing my brain to accommodate new Turkish words plus new mathematical equations. After all music is only another form of maths with sound.

Another urgent phone call to the publishing company in New York to get another copy of the Conductor's Copy of the music sent here ASAP. Again, they assured the Chaplain that another copy was in the mail today, special delivery. In the meantime, what in the hell am I supposed to do. In short, you memorise, memorise and memorise. To the many thousands that have never been exposed to the needs of such discipline of memorisation I'll say don't try it. Once it has been firmly imprinted into your memory bank you will carry it to your grave. Case in point. Take the selection *For Unto Us A Child Is Born* from the *Messiah* and in your mind it comes out like this. Orchestra, one beat followed by the Soprano's singing . . . *For Unto Us A Child Is Born*, two beats before the next passage starts . . . Sopranos *Unto Us* . . . one and a half beats . . . *A Son Is Given* . . . two beats . . . enter tenors *For Unto Us A Child* . . . enter sopranos *For Unto Us*, tenors *Is Born* two beats . . . etc. Now you take the entire programme which you are doing and master all the moving parts for the orchestra and the four vocal parts and you have one hell of a human computer buzzing in your head from start to finish. Now if you really want to have fun take the *Amen Chorus* at the end of the *Messiah* when the orchestra takes off in one direction while the four vocal parts take off in four entirely different directions all at the same time. There you are, standing in the middle of all this, no music in front of you with all parts committed to your brain, with

136

only your two hands, two eyes and your two ears. All you have in the way of support is that which you have committed to your brain and its memory. At this point you pray to God that you don't have a short circuit lurking around the corner some place, because you haven't got a prayer in hell. As the director of this massive group of people it is your responsibility to blend them into the perfect performing musical ensemble with the pride of the Turkish nation and the United States hanging in the balance. Just how in the friggin' hell did I manage to get myself into this mess. After weeks of rehearsals and we are still far from our goal. Today I feel sick. Not sick, sick, but just sick. Five days before the Concert and I still haven't received my Conductor's Copy of the *Messiah*. Between you and me, my poor little brain is yelling, stop, stop, I've had enough. More than once I have found myself giving musical instructions in English to the all Turkish speaking Orchestra and Turkish musical instructions to the all speaking English, Choral Group. This may seem all very funny, but it is very serious revealing an overworked and tired mind. I'm physically tired but I haven't missed a beat with my military duties and have kept all systems going. I think that I'm getting off side with Hanna. Just this morning she was scolding and laying the law down to me about skipping my meals and losing weight. 'Look *Mösyöciğim*,' she continued, 'your face is no pretty, you no smile, you no laugh. You are becoming like teeth wood, (she means tooth pick), and that is no pretty. You big man, you big eat. With so much riding on this concert and the pressures building up as each day passes, who cares and who has time to eat. My God, two days to go and still no Conductor's Copy of the music. As I look skyward the little voice keeps coming back saying . . . 'cram . . . cram . . . cram . . . you fool.' It has gotten to the point that I'm waking up during the middle of the night going over passages which seemingly require more work. I get up, go into the living room, put on the recording and go over and over the passage until such time that it is firmly embedded into my memory cells. After that, it's back to bed and wide awake.

Tonight is our first dress rehearsal. The five newspapers *Cumhuriyt, Milliyet, Tercuman, Yenisabah* and *Vatan* have all carried stories about this Turkish – American Concert as well as sending their photographers to obtain photographs of this now built up super special spectacle which was to come to pass in two nights. Frankly, I thought of it as more of my demise and nothing of special interest to write about and only hoped that they wrote nice things about me when I was gone.

137

Our first dress rehearsal was nothing but a series of stop and go while changing this and changing that. Stressing the points of their attacks and their releases.

'I would like to see all soloist women here please. Now ladies, do not wear any dress that may just wipe out part of the string section when making your way to centre stage. One more thing ladies, when you get to the podium stop, as that is where I'll be standing and I'm not going to move off of it for you. Do I make myself clear? Fine.'

Look at the time. It is now nearing midnight and there is still a long way to go before this even faintly resembles an organised mess. It's now nearing 0100 hours and things seem to be a little better than they were an hour ago. On the other hand maybe it's because I want to think that they are better to give me a bit of encouragement to be able to face tomorrow.

'Okay people, let's call it a night. Remember, be here at 1800 hours sharp as that will be our last chance to really try and get this all put together. You know Chaplain, you would think that I was asking them for the moon when I tell them to be here on time. I can understand that they are tired, but by the same token I kid you not, I'm completely exhausted. Again Chaplain, many thanks for bringing me home. I'll see you tomorrow afternoon about 1730 hours.'

Now for a good quick shower and hit the hay. These were my thoughts as I was climbing the stairway to my apartment. As I open the door I see the little table lamp is on and a note on the table. '*Mösyöciğim*, it reads, 'you big eat'. . . sighed Hanna. After 1.00 a.m. in the morning, who in the hell wants to eat and then go to bed? What I need is a nice shower then press the sheets with my body before it is time to get up and start all over again. As for food, I'll get up, put some food in a plastic bag, and take it to work with me before Hanna gets here and she will be none the wiser. Oh Lord, with all this going on around me, without any hesitation I could very easily become paranoid. However, I just haven't got the time, and besides, it won't fit into my schedule.

Morning arrives all too soon and I really wasn't ready to face the day with all its variables. With a little stretch this way and a little scratch that way and ah, it did feel real good. As I was lying there a little voice said to me, hay buster, get your ass in gear and get the hell out of bed. Nasty little voice ought to have its little ass kicked up between it's shoulders as it has no right speaking to me like that. After having made this remark I began to fully understand that it was the voice of my subconscious mind telling me that I had gone back to sleep and it was doing it's level best to get me moving again. Now that I'm fully awake, I'm running a bit late. Thank God there was water this morning along with gas, so shaving was quick. Now for a quick cup of coffee and some of Hanna's cooking from last night safely placed in a plastic bag, I'm ready to hit the road.

'Hi Serg, I see that you made the Turkish morning newspapers again with pictures of you and your group. When you get finished you'll be as well known as some of the local movie stars.'

'See ya later.' I just wonder how many other shit asses are going to bring this newspaper business up again today? I had better call the Chaplain to see if my copy of the *Messiah* has arrived today. It will seem most funny to many concert-goers to see a Symphony Orchestra being conducted without the music in front of the conductor. Between thee and me, I think it's damn right hilarious and hysterical, so what hypothesis can be drawn from that? This whole thing would be real funny and laughable except for the fact that the shoe is on my foot. Oh God, please let the musical score arrive.

'Good afternoon Chaplain, have we had any help from the man upstairs?'

'Who is this?'

'Chaplain, who do you think would be asking for divine intervention at a time like this?'

'Oh Carl, it's you.'

'Excuse me Chaplain, but from whom do you think would be asking for divine intervention?'

'Carl, I went to the APO (Army Post Office) today to see the Officer-In-Charge Captain Albright, and he told me that should it arrive into the APO prior to the concert that he would personally bring it to the concert hall. That's very nice of him to do this, should it arrive, but like my dear old papa once told me, "son, only bet your money on sure things.' In the next breath he said to me, 'son don't ever bet on life, as that is the poorest bet of all.'"

'Okay Chaplain, I'll be waiting for you to pick me up on Atatürk Boulevarde at about 1745 hours. Again, many thanks for your help and your support.'

I had better check into the Puzzle Palace upstairs to see if any great events have unfolded during the time that I was out of the headquarters. I feel certain that no one would want to blow this place up and end all of this confusion which abounds from these walls daily.

'Hi Faye, how are things in your shop today?' (I've learned a long time ago if you want to know what is going on around here just ask Faye). The old saying is, 'Do you know the three fastest means of communications? . . . ' Answer, Telephone, Telegraph and tell Faye.

'Carl, I heard today through the grapevine that one of the secretaries in the headquarters has been picked up on Black Market charges and was taken in for questioning.'

'You don't say.'

'Further, I'm told, she had made a number of purchases from the Post Exchange, took them home and then sold them to her maid. Of course what she didn't know was that her maid was working for the Secret Police and the Turkish Officials ratted on her to the OSI (Overseas Secret Investigation).

'Well, that's what they told me.'

'If it's true, it is rather sad as she was one of the better secretaries downstairs.'

'Thanks Faye.'

Now do you know the three fastest means of communication? . . . you should. I didn't want to spoil Faye's reporting, but there was another secretary also involved in this matter. She worked upstairs and was even here when I arrived in the old JAMMAT. If anyone should have known better it was she. Between thee and the lamp post, I would sooner think that this secretary talked the other secretary into this situation. In this type of military business, you just never know who is who or what is what. I could tell you a number of things that I found out just by accident. Like I said, in this business you just never really know who your bed partner is, figuratively speaking. I had worked with this Turkish man for over a year day in and day out and only by accident I learned he was one of the top men in Interpol in Ankara. That surely came as one hell of a surprise to me but his secret was safe with me. It all goes to prove one very important point. Don't even trust your grandmother as she too could be on someone's secret payroll.

'Sergeant Crocker,' the good Major says with a smile on his face. 'Do you have everything under control for tomorrow night's concert?'

'Yes, I do believe I have, but of course that is by no means with the help of this headquarters or the US Embassy, Sir. Thank you for your concern. I had better get out of his office before I lose control of myself, jump up and stand on his desk and piss all over his official papers.

'Yep Chaplain, we are right on time. Thank goodness the traffic

140

through Yenişhier wasn't too bad this evening or we may have been late. Needless to say, they would surely let me know that I was late after telling them to be here at 1800 hours sharp. All right people, let's take our places so we can get this last rehearsal on the road. You know Chaplain, there seems to be a lot of buzzing around of people who doesn't belong here at this time. Look over there.'

'Yes, I see what you mean.'

'Maybe once we get started they will rack off. Take your places people. Move, don't stand there beating your gums, as we have a very long way to go and only tonight to get it all put together. Chaplain, there must be something going on here that we don't know about. Now look out into the Lobby area and you can see there are a lot of people with plenty of discussion going on. It would appear that they are working out various angles of some kind. Where is Metin my concert master? Has anyone seen Metin?'

'Carl, I think that someone said that Metin would be a little late as he had to take his daughter to the doctor.'

'Currently, I'm running on nervous energy and the tank is getting low. Look at that. Now what in hell is that man doing just over my podium?'

'It looks like he is hanging a microphone down from the ceiling which will be just a bit to the right of your head and a little bit higher.'

'I wonder if they expect me to swing on it or hang myself should something go radically wrong? Damn it to hell, we have been here for twenty-five minutes and extravagantly squandered all this time and not one note or melodious chord has been sounded. This just won't cut it. Time right now is my worse enemy. Chaplain, do you see that man over there who seems to be shouting directions across the concert hall? No, not that one, the one dressed nicely in civilian clothing.'

'Oh yes.'

'Would you mind asking him to please come and have a word with me? Thanks.'

'Good evening sir. Do you speak English?'

'Yes I do.'

'Can you please explain to me just what is going on out in the auditorium area with all the people shouting at one another?'

'Yes I can. You see Sergeant Crocker . . .'

'Hold it right there. How do you know my name?'

'Please let me finish Sergeant Crocker. I'm Inspector Erol from the

Turkish State Secret Police and we are here to safeguard President General Cemal Gürsel, the Prime Minister and the Turkish Cabinet. You may not be aware of it, but you are very well known here in the political, diplomatic and Military Circles for that which you are doing here.'

'I really do not understand what you are on about or what you are talking about.'

'It is very obvious and understandable now that no one has told you anything about what has been transpiring inside or outside of Turkey which had to be combated both strongly and firmly but still quietly.'

'Inspector Erol, I don't mean to be disrespectful to you but you have left me in the starting gate figuratively speaking. I don't understand all of the ramifications which you are trying to relate to me.'

'Sergeant Crocker, let me put it another way. Firstly, you must have heard about all of the problems we are having on Cyprus with the Cypriot Greeks and how they are saying that the United States are siding with them. To offset that, we were showing the Greeks, that we had very excellent and strong ties with America and NATO not only militarily but also culturally. What better way to do this than to have an American Sergeant direct our Presidential Symphony Orchestra with your American chorus and have our President, Prime Minister and the Cabinet in attendance.'

'Inspector Erol, would you mind if I sit down as this crap or this revelation is sort of getting beyond my comprehension at this point in time. I'm tired, and my little one cell brain has just about had the course. If I'm incorrect, please stop me. What you are saying in simple terms is that I was selected as a pawn in this massive game of world diplomacy to take centre stage. Inspector Erol, is that what you are saying?'

'Yes Sergeant Crocker. I should add if this is any consolation, but before you were selected for this special project, your background was checked with the American OSI,' our Turkish Security National Police, and Interpol. When all had been checked out and you were found to be most acceptable, we had our Minister of Cultural Affairs make the initial contact.'

'I have just one question. What part did the American Ambassador play in this game of deception?'

'He was notified by our President's Office of our intent and was asked to inform the Secretary of State in Washington DC for his approval to use you.'

'Thank you Inspector Erol, that explains a number of things to me. It would appear that I was much too harsh on the Ambassador for his part in this episode. Please continue Inspector Erol.'

'As I was saying, all the newspapers in Athens, London, Nicosia, Washington DC and Ankara will know and understand that we have close working relations with America or else such a project of close requirements would and could not have been possible. It is hoped that this will dispel any misgivings these people may have been harbouring concerning America and Turkey.'

'Inspector Erol, I still don't understand all of this. What brought this about?'

'The best I can make of it is that your President Johnson on a number of occasions opened his mouth in public on sensitive issues with criticism being directed towards Turkey which really was not warranted. Senator Barry Goldwater, on the other hand, took the President to task over the issues. A split with one of NATO members was well in the offing. This would have caused untold damage to NATO's Southern flank. What made this situation so explosive was the fact that your President was siding with Greece over Cyprus when he shouldn't have been saying or siding with anyone. Of course you understand Sergeant Crocker this entire operation of which we have just spoken must remain secret. At the proper time either Washington DC or Ankara will release this information. However, any leak concerning this information will only mean heads will roll. As for my part, I have told you absolutely nothing and that is my official stand. I do hope that I make myself clear, don't I?'

'Yes Inspector Erol, very.'

There I sat in the third row in the Concert Hall trying as best I could to digest and comprehend all which has just gone before me. Me, a Mister Nobody, end up being an integral part of this massive jigsaw puzzle. Sure, I like the country of Turkey very much and I dearly love its people. They have proved to be honest, loyal and in general really wonderful people. Now as I see it, my honesty and loyalty towards Turkey and its people has been placed squarely on the line. Can I, and will I, be worthy of this task which has been placed before me? I don't know, only in a short time will history say yes or no, and I mean a short time . . . tomorrow night.

'Okay people, we have used up more than enough valuable time milling around like cattle, so let's get stuck into some real hard work.'

The sudden stampede of musical instruments with people attached to them and the chorus moving all at once would give you the impression of the Great San Francisco Earthquake. I haven't seen people move so fast around here since the last outbreak of diarrhoea.

Orkestra.

'*Birinci musik sayfanizi orkesra ve koro ile gevirin. Son Dört parçayi koro gelmeden önce bascayin.* OK? *Tamam?*'

Chorus. 'Start at the beginning of Behold The Lamb of God. Now watch your attacks and releases.'

Orkestra. 'Ve bir.'

Chorus. 'Sopranos. Behold The Lamb of God.

'Sopranos hold it. Didn't I just tell you to watch your attack on your first note? You slid into it like a seal crying and sliding in for a dead fish. Can't you hear what you are doing? Wake up. Think. This will hold true for the tenors, altos and basses. Now start thinking up and over your tones, and above all don't sit on them. Remember people, your opening chorus can either make or break the entire programme. As a matter of fact, if you are serious and interested in what you are singing, the audience will be interested in what you are relating to them which forms an interaction. Once that has been achieved, your communications have been established. Okay people, I'm sure you have gotten the message, so let's go once again.'

Orkestra. Make your notes sharp and crisp as well. (There I go again, telling them in English when it should be in Turkish).

Orkestra. Notalarinizi keskin ve güzel yapiniz.

Okay, *Orkestra. Bir* (one) (beat).

Chorus. Behold The Lamb of God.

Good, good. Think up and over your tones.

Keep it going until the end . . . Tenors.

Good, good. For the first time you all sounded like you really enjoyed singing this selection. Just keep that vibrant sound coming and you'll be home scot free. It sounded just great. Okay people, we have been going for nearly two hours without a break, so let's take a short one. Further, let me say one thing more before we break. For the first time I felt like you sounded like a complete musical group instead of 85 individual voices trying to outdo each other. Keep it up.'

'Sergeant Crocker.'

'Yes, Inspector Erol.'

'I was watching you just a few minutes ago and honestly speaking,

I had no idea or comprehension of the complexity of this special project.'

'Complexity, Inspector Erol? My good sir, complexity isn't the half of it.'

'I noticed that you didn't have any music in front of you, was that for any reason?'

'The answer to your question is yes, but let's not talk about complexities.'

'Well . . . how do you do it?'

'With much much difficulty Inspector Erol.'

Look at the time. We have been hard at it for the past four and a half hours. I must have worn them to a frazzle, but frankly I think it's the other way around. Well, whichever way it is I'm nearly too pooped to pop and that's tired.

'Okay people, you have responded well, so let's call it a night. One thing more before we break and that is to be here early so we can have a good warm up and then relax. Oh yes, I would like a word with the women soloists for just a minute or two. Thank you all very much again. Anne, Claire, Tula and Jane I want to check again to ensure that none of you lovely ladies are wearing dresses made from taffeta. As you can see, with all these microphones placed around the stage, any movement with a taffeta dress would sound like breakfast cereal, snap, crackle and pop. Thanks again for all your efforts.'

'Oh Chaplain, did the Turkish printer deliver the programmes to your office today? Good. I don't know about you Chaplain Wilson, but I'm just plain physically, mentally and spiritually exhausted.'

'I can understand it Carl, trying to keep up with your military duties during the day and taking this activity on at night would send the average person around the bend.'

'I can tell you Chaplain, I'm not too far from that point right now. In short, let's get out of here. I'm very happy in some ways that tomorrow is the opening night plus being a Saturday which means for the first time in a very long time I'm not rushing to rehearsals. Since Hanna doesn't come tomorrow, I'm going to lie in bed until I'm ready to get up.'

Oh no! It's only 0700 hours and Hanna is here. Maybe if I pretend that I'm asleep, she will go away. Better yet, I'll just pull the sheets over my head and hope for the best. With a singing voice I hear . . . 'Good morning my *Mösyöciğim*, you no sleepy all day?'

'All day Hanna, I just got into bed a short while ago and now you want me to get up. What I didn't tell her was that when I arrived home I was going to take a quick shower, but as usual we didn't have any water. So I did the next best thing and took a birdie bath and jumped into bed stark naked. Now there she stands waiting for me to get up so she can get the sheets. Silly woman. 'Hanna, are you going to the kitchen to make some coffee?'

'No *Mösyöciğim*, I want sheets to wash.'

What can I do to get her mind off of these sheets? 'By the way Hanna, today is Saturday and you should be at your Madam's.'

'*Mösyöciğim*, I know today is Saturday, I days can count. You think me *dili* . . . ? (crazy).'

'No..no Hanna *dili deyil*.' (Crazy you are not).

'Then why you no bed get out of so I can work?'

God I thought, isn't there any justice left in this world?'

'You no bed get out of, I go make coffee for you.'

'Thank you Hanna.' That was just too close for comfort. Remind me never to do that again.

'That's good *Mösyöciğim*, you now up. I was thinking you in bed stay all day.' I would have liked to have had a few more hours sleep, but that has gone by the wayside.

'By the way Hanna, do you know what your Madam did last night?'

'Oh yes, she was going to the big general's party last night at the Subay Klüb.' (Officers Club).

'Yes Hanna, I'm getting the big picture.'

'What picture *Mösyöciğim*? I no picture see?'

'I guess your Madam gets home late sometimes after attending the big general's party?'

'Yes *Mösyöciğim*, party sometimes very late.'

'Now I can understand why your Madam wanted you to come and help me this morning.'

'What you speaking *Mösyöciğim*?'

'Nothing Hanna, I was just thinking out loud.'

'Funny speaking.' Just wait until I see Joyce. However, I guess her intentions were good, but I sure could have used some more sleep.

'*Mösyöciğim*, your black suit no more smell now.'

'I know Hanna, I have had it hanging out on the back balcony for the past six days just to get the damn smell out of it. The cleaning fluid this time smelled like gasoline mixed with kerosene and what an odour it gave off. I couldn't keep it inside for fear it would blow up in case someone came in smoking. One day, I keep telling myself, things will change for the better.

'Hanna, I'm going to take a Dolmus and go down to the Post Exchange at the Car Barn Area.'

'*Mösyöciğim*, why you no take taxi?'

'Hanna, it's more fun in the Dolmus.'

'Yes *Mösyöciğim*, my Poppie say he like to take Dolmus so he can play with girls bottoms.' To Hanna, pitching is playing so you would have to understand this terminology through her way of thinking. 'I'll see you a little later Hanna.'

'Oh *Mösyöciğim*, you better go Commissary and bring some paprika, coffee, flour, garlic powder, salt and don't forget paper towels. See what I mean?' I live there but see who runs the house and me?

'Hi Chaplain, what brings you to this people-infested area today?'

I received a telephone call from Captain Albright this morning and he asked me to come here to meet him.'

'Did he say what he wanted?'

'As a matter of fact he did. He rang me to tell me that your music for the *Messiah* had arrived by special courier from the Turkish Custom's Office.'

'From where?'

'The Turkish Custom's Office here in Ankara. Would you believe there are two copies of the Conductor's Music. It seems that whoever mailed it in New York addressed it to the Choral Group, Ankara, Turkey. Of course customs in their wisdom didn't know where it was supposed to go. It was held there for customs payment. One employee by chance read in the Turkish Newspaper that the *Messiah* was to be given as a concert so their director notified the Minister of Education. Someone, we don't know whom, finally put two and two together and came up with the correct answer. I don't know if custom duties were paid on them or not, or if they will end up on my personal Bayanname. I'll cross that bridge when I come to it.'

'I can understand precisely how you feel relating to this subject, but what the heck, let's have a cup of coffee and relax for a few minutes.'

'Anyway, Captain Albright said that he would bring them to me.'

'Thank him for me, but tell him he didn't have to hurry now on my account. Six hours from now is the start of the concert and I'm going to worry about the Conductor's Copy of the music? No way.'

'Carl, I thought that we were going to have that cup of coffee and relax?'

'You're absolutely right Chaplain. By the way, look who just came in the front door. Yep, it's Joyce Backhouse. You go get her Chaplain and I'll go and get her a cup of coffee.' As I come back to the table I can see that she has a big smile on her face and she greets me with 'and how did your day start off?'My reply was with a little smirk on my face '. . . with a bang.' With that answer, Joyce just threw her head back and let out with a loud roar. With both of us knowing Hanna as we do, no word of explanation was necessary. Still smiling she asked, if I was ready for tonight's concert. Without thinking, as I usually do at times, I said, 'as ready as a prostitute in a brothel.' With that answer, Joyce and I really started to laugh, rather loudly I might add, forgetting that we were sitting at the table with the Chaplain. With a sip of coffee here and a sip of coffee there, Joyce and I managed to compose ourselves somewhat until I told the story about a young farmer and his bride to-be on a farm back in the mid-west. As the story goes, young farmer Jim wanted to get married to a young girl named Lucy-May, a farm girl herself. Lucy-May lived on the farm with her widowed mother. Since these were very hard times, Lucy-May's mama thought she could talk to the minister and have them married in his church and it wouldn't cost them any money. Further, after they were married, they could come and live in her farmhouse and try to save a bit of money. Further, Lucy-May's mum would even go so far as to have a lovely wedding supper in her home for them. When the day arrived all went according to schedule and the day was just beautiful. After the evening meal Lucy-May started to help her mama as she had always done to do the washing up and drying the dishes. Part way through the regular evening ritual Lucy-May's mama remembered that this was her daughter's wedding night. She said, Lucy-May you go upstairs to be with Jim on your wedding night. When she arrived upstairs she found Jim with his shirt off revealing his fully beautiful muscular brawny chest which was so inviting, the likes of which she had never seen before. Her heart pumped faster and faster and she nearly went out of her mind. She removed her dress with a nervousness she had never known before. Jim removed his trousers and the next move was hers. Hardly able to contain herself, she removed her slip and her bra revealing two beautifully firm breasts. 'Oh Jim,' she said, as he removed his undershorts, 'it's beautiful.' She removed her panties while heading for the bed, meeting

148

Jim half way. Now fully stretched out, lying on the bed, she nervously awaited his muscular touch. Looking down she saw that Jim had not removed his socks. 'Please Jim, she pleaded, take off your socks.' Slowly Jim reached down and took off one sock. 'Please Jim,' she pleaded 'take off your other sock.'

'Why darling, does it make such a difference?'

'Jim I want you completely undressed so I can always remember this night.'

'Well, if that's what will please you Lucy-May.' He reaches down and removes the other sock.

'Oh my God.' she screamed as she saw only a half a foot. Grabbing her dressing gown, she ran downstairs screaming, 'Mama, Mama.' Mama was in the kitchen drying the dishes and turned to see what the matter was with Lucy May. 'Oh Mama, Mama she sobbed, it's just horrible.'

'Now Lucy-May you just calm down honey and tell Mama what the problem is.'

'It's Jim.'

'What's wrong with Jim,' she demanded.

'He has . . . he has . . . '

'Lucy-May you just calm down now honey and tell Mama what's so wrong.'

'It's Jim Mama, he has a foot and a half, and it's just horrible.

'Now Lucy-May, you just calm down honey, and take this dish towel and dry the dishes. I'll go upstairs and take care of Jim's foot and a half.'

Not noticing the other two tables close to ours the people sitting there had their ear antennae tuned into my story. When I hit the punch line all hell broke loose. Would you believe that even the snack bar manager came over to our table and wanted to know if everything was alright. Remind me not to tell any more stories there.

'Joyce and Chaplain, I know you all have things to do so I won't keep you any longer. I guess I had better get the items that Hanna wanted from the Commissary, or I had just better stay here until she leaves for home. I'll see you later. What time are you stopping by this evening Chaplain?'

'The usual.'

'Thanks.'

'Joyce, I'll see you tonight at the concert with Hanna. Take care.'

'By the way Carl, what shall I do with the music?'

'I could tell you Chaplain, but I'm a gentleman. I guess you should bring one copy just to keep from blowing too many people's minds. They just wouldn't understand that I have all the music for tonight's programme all locked up in my head. Let's hope that nothing happens to my head. See ya.'

'*Mösyöciğim*, you to me everything bring?'

'Yes Hanna, everything to you I brought.' (Just stopped by her to have one quick lesson on how to murder the English language).

'Hanna, if you want you may leave early today so you can meet your Madam for the concert this evening.'

'Everything here finished nearly. When translated means, I'm hot to trot. 'Okay Hanna, I'll see you this evening.'

'Thank you *Mösyöciğim*.'

Now for a little peace and quiet before the onslaught of this evening. Little did I realise then what fate had in store for me before the night was finished.

As I put the body in the prone position for a short while, I set the alarm and headed off to dream land. What a wonderful feeling of being transformed into the arms of Morpheus and leaving all these earthly cares behind. All too soon the damn alarm brings me back to earth and the realities I must again face.

As I see it, I now have about twenty-five minutes before I meet the Chaplain up on Atatürk Blvd. Shall I wear one ring or two rings. I'll follow my instinct and really look flashy. Since this is my night to shine, why not blind them. That is a real cheap remark from me as I close the door and head up the street.

When we get there I want to have a good warm up for both the Choral Group and the Orchestra. After that I want them all to relax as I'm sure that things will fall into their proper places.

'Sounds good to me Carl.'

'I'll place your Conductor's Copy of your music on your stand.'

'Thanks Chaplain.'

'All right people, we have a lot of quick and hard work to accomplish in just a few minutes. After that, I want all of you to relax so you will feel fresh when you arrive on stage. One other thing. During the intermission, I do not want to be disturbed by anyone. All I want is a glass of water, and to be left alone so I can concentrate on the second half of the programme. Do I make myself clear? Good. Now let's start *Worthy Is A Lamb* and go right into the *Amen* . . . Excellent, excellent . . . People, you have never sounded better. We'll break now and you just relax. There are plenty of programmes to go around so just relax and I'll see everyone soon.'

'Chaplain Wilson, may I borrow the keys to your car so I can get my coat out?'

'That's right, you did leave it there when we got out of the car.'

'Yes.'

'I'll be just a minute as there are a few little problems that should be addressed prior to going on stage.'

Now which key is it? I sure would have been much easier if I hadn't dropped the damn keys in the first place. Oh well don't cry over dropped keys Carl. Now this must be the one. Yep, it's so much easier when you have the correct key. 'Stop where you are,' said a voice in Turkish. 'What are you doing here?'

'I'm getting my coat out of the car as you can plainly see,' I answered in Turkish.

'Don't you know that this is a Security Area and no one is allowed to be in here?'

'I don't know about that, I just came to get my coat.'

'That's a very likely story,' the Security Guard growled at me. 'Lean against the car,' he commanded, 'and put your hands on top of the roof.' Since he had a gun in his hand, I was convinced he meant business. Of course I wouldn't know what would give me such an idea.

'Okay . . . okay I'm leaning against the car.'

With the flick of his wrist I suddenly find that I'm the unsuspecting and unceremonious wearer of one set of chrome plated handcuffs.

'Now damn it, hold it.' I shouted at him in Turkish.

'Shut up,' he said. 'Since you are in an unauthorised area and at the time that our President and Prime Minister are due here, you could be a terrorist for all we know.'

'You have gotten it all wrong I protested. I'm the conductor of the Orchestra and the Choral Group that are performing for your President and Prime Minister here tonight.'

'Don't make me laugh, and I'm taking you to the Police Command Van until we can find out who you are and the truth.'

'I'm telling you the truth. Take me to the Concert Hall,' I yelled, 'I'm the Conductor for tonight's programme.'

'I told you to shut up, and that's what I mean. You may just end up going to jail and getting all of your hair cut off. You sure will be good looking then.' He motioned like he was going to hit me as he pushed his pistol into my back with force. I called him a 'son-of-a-bitch' in English, but he didn't seem to understand. Perhaps it was just as well he didn't. As I sat inside the large Police Command Van I looked at the ceiling and started to laugh. As I laughed, tears came slowly down my cheeks. My God, I thought, I must have reached my stress level as I had never in my life ever felt or been in such a position of helplessness like I now find myself. As I laughed, I said to the Security Police, 'just wait you bastard until the concert is ready to commence and the President and the Prime Minister are told that the conductor cannot be found and they will have to go home. Funny isn't it?'

'I told you to shut up, don't you understand Turkish?' as he shoved me against the van wall. When he shoved me, my head struck a sharp protruding object on the right side of my head just above my right ear. When I leaned forward from the pain of being struck, he shoved me back once again and the sharp object struck my head the second time. Sitting there with my head bent forward, I just can't believe in my wildest thoughts that this is happening to me. Raising my hands to the general area which hurt, I feel something wet. Oh God, as I bring my hands down, I find that I have been smearing my own blood all over the back of my neck and my shirt. If that wasn't enough, these damn handcuffs are bruising and cutting into my wrists. Funny thoughts enter your mind when at a time like this, logic seems to vanish and the flood gates seem to open letting in all sort of ideas. Now I understand only too well just how other soldiers felt in days gone by when fighting red Indians and waiting and praying for the Horse Cavalry to come storming in to save them. Well, this is Turkey and there are no red Indians or Horse Cavalry to come to my rescue. Suddenly, I think I hear a familiar voice saying that the President's vehicle has just arrived followed by the Prime Minister's. I try to see what's going on, but the damn Security Policy pushed me back against the van's wall once again and again I hit my head on that sharp object. Just what I need, another hole in my head. I've made up my mind that this bastard is going to pay for it dearly. The Security Van door opens and in steps Inspector Erol.

'Inspector,' I shouted.

'Sergeant Crocker,' he countered, with a horrible look on his face, 'just what in the hell are you doing here, and in handcuffs. My God, you are hurt and bleeding. What happened?'

'May I highly suggest you ask that "Pea Brain" Security Officer right there what happened.'

'Ahmet, explain what happened.'

'It's like this Inspector Erol. We were making our rounds and saw this man in the parking lot with a shining object in his hands. We thought it was or could be a gun so we rushed him and then brought him here.'

'Where is the shining object now?'

'We didn't find the gun, but he must have thrown it away.'

'Did this man tell you that he was the conductor of our Presidential Symphony Orchestra?'

'Yes, but we didn't believe him, because he wasn't Turkish.'

'Did he ask to be brought to the Concert Hall?'

'Yes, but we thought it was just a trick to make his get away.'

'To whom have you reported this incident?'

'Nobody yet, as we were going to do it after the concert.'

'After the concert? You stupid peasant, without this man there is no concert. Unlock the handcuffs.'

'I can't sir, as I think we left the key at Central Headquarters.'

'Send someone there to get it damn quick.'

'Yes sir.'

'Come this way Sergeant Crocker, we have an ambulance here with a medical doctor that can take care of your wounds.' 'Doctor Mehmet, this is Sergeant Crocker and I think from the looks of him he will need your professional help.'

'Thank you Inspector Erol and Dr Mehmet.'

Shortly Dr Mehmet had me all patched up.

'Sergeant Crocker, I'll take you back to the Concert Hall.'

'Just a minute Inspector Erol. I'm not going any place but home. I've had quite enough for one night to last me a lifetime. Inspector Erol let me say now that it is not your fault or that of the Secret Police, but rather two individuals who wanted to make a name for themselves but didn't know how to do it. Look at me, blood, my blood, smeared all over the back of me like a common cheap criminal. Look at both wrists. Look at them, bruised and also bleeding. I've endured a number of hardships during my military career, but nothing so degrading, humiliating and disgusting as what has happened this evening. I'm not trying to be something I'm not, but I just can't go into the concert hall and face my group looking like this.'

'There you are Carl. What in God's name has happened to you? When you didn't return, I came out looking for you but you were nowhere to be found.'

'It is quite obvious you didn't meet up with Ahmet and his Abi (brother) from the Security Police like I did.'

'You still have the keys to my car don't you?'

'As a matter of fact Chaplain, no I haven't. When the two Police jerked me around I went in one direction and your keys went flying in another direction. However, they shouldn't be too far from the car.'

'How do you feel Carl?'

'Do you really want me to tell you?'

'On second thought, I'll withdraw that question.'

'Chaplain, I think that we should go back to the parking lot to see if we can find your keys. Look, my coat is still in the car. If we look towards the front part of the car, we should find the car keys. Yep, true to form there are your shining keys hanging from that bush over there. Pistol? Inspector Erol, there is your shining pistol, the car keys. I think that the two of them should have their eyes examined. Better yet, I believe that they should have their heads examined.'

'Inspector Erol, here are the keys to the handcuffs.'

'It took you long enough, what did you have to do make them?'

'No sir, we couldn't find them.'

'That will be all Ahmet until later.'

We all enter by the side door of the concert hall and I can see the extent of the mess I'm in. As we enter opposite the stage, half of the orchestra and the chorus can see me not looking too well with blood still on me. Now if you think that there was movement at the OK Corral, you should have seen the movement on stage at the Devilet Koser Salonu. At this point, the Director of the Devilet Koser Salonu has taken centre stage telling the invited guests and the standing room only audience that due to a small technical problem, there would be only a very slight delay before starting the programme. To be sure, the technical problem was never revealed. A quick conference was called just off stage to save face with all concerned, namely the government. At this point in time, I didn't want anything to do with anybody. I just wanted to go home and get away from it all. Chaplain Wilson sat looking at me and didn't want to enter into my thoughts. I'm sure he understood my feelings. As I sat there looking at the people on stage, I wondered just how many times they wanted to walk out after I had given them a brow-beating after each rehearsal? Oh my God, this was sure soul-searching time for all concerned, namely me. Finally swallowing my pride and my hurt, I said that I would go on with the concert. A new white shirt was found and my wrists were bandaged to hide the handcuff marks.A hush fell over the audience as the Director of the Devilet Konser Salonu took centre stage again. Mr President, Mr Prime Minister, Ladies and Gentlemen, our technical difficulties have been corrected and I thank you for your indulgence.

Pulling myself together, which was a damn hard thing to do, I entered the stage to a loud ovation. The Orchestra and Choral Group also stood up as I placed a smile on my face. I thought, as long as I had a smile on my face no one would ever know what had taken place out in the police van or what I was really thinking. I acknowledged the President with a bow, the Prime Minister with a bow and then the Cabinet also with a bow. Next I turned to face all the Ambassadors representing 28 heads of government including 'Old Bunny', better known as Ambassador Blair. I next turned to acknowledge the rest of the standing room only audience. After accepting their applause I turned and stepped on to the podium. The Orchestra and Choral Group then seated themselves. I opened my conductor's musical score which I had never seen before and reached for my baton. Baton . . . my baton . . . where in hell is my baton . . . my symbol of authority. That's a laugh after what has happened to me this evening. I look at my Concert Master and his face was as red as a spanked baby's ass. He is supposed to be the person who places my baton on my music stand. This whole mess reminds me of Murphy's Law . . . anything that can go wrong will go wrong. I can tell you unequivocally right here and now, that something had better start happening right. I smiled at my group, taking both hands tapping my rings on each side of the music stand and we were ready to get this show on the proverbial road.

The Overture really sounded good. Their attacks and releases were just great. The rest of the choral selections have been just excellent. I just don't believe everything is falling into place at the right time. Now we'll complete the *Hallelujah Chorus* and have a fifteen minute break. At this point I seek out my Concert Master Metin to see what has happened to my baton.

'Sir,' he says, 'on my way to the stage I stopped in the toilet to relieve myself and forgot your baton in the toilet. I'm very embarrassed, as I have never done that before.'

'Don't worry Metin, it never happened to me before either.' Now I'll get my glass of water and go and find a quiet place to think about the second half of the programme.'

This feels good just to get away from everyone.

'Excuse me Mr Crocker, I have a lady here who wants to speak to you.'

'Do you remember what I told all of you during the warm up rehearsal?'

'Yes sir, but this lady has insisted in speaking with you.' She threw her name, but I was in no frame of mind to catch it and let it go at that.

'Young man,' she continued, 'do you know what you are doing?' I thought, shit lady, if I don't know what I'm doing at this stage of the game, I had better fold up my tent and go home. She went on, 'I'll tell you what you are doing. What you are doing is worth millions, and no amount of money could possibly buy what you are doing. My father was the first American Ambassador to Turkey and we would have given anything to have had something like this occur. You are doing something that has never been done before. I just wanted to meet you and to thank you for your efforts.' Efforts I thought to myself. Lady, you don't know the half of it. I did manage to thank her for her kind words. What has happened to your wrists? They look a little sore.'

'Yes they are.'

'Thank you for speaking with me.'

'My pleasure madam.' Now for another drink of water and it's back to centre stage.

To start off the second half of the programme I have the soprano air '*I Know That My Redeemer Liveth*.' She did a very nice job with the solo and it seems that the people appreciated it. With a click, click in my head tells me that the chorus comes now with *Since By Man Came Death*'. I now point to Unal, my Bass Viol player. He has one very important solo note which starts the entire chorus off. I point to him once again. He smiles at me once more. What in the hell is he doing? I point once more and once more I get a very lovely smile but no note. I look at Metin and he is just about to come over the music racks and bounce him on his head. I'll give him another try. Same response. Damn it, I can't keep pointing all night, or we'll never get this concert over with. In sheer desperation I look to my bass section as one of my basses has perfect pitch. Bud, Bud, where are you now that I need you? When he sees that I'm in deep serious trouble I faintly hear the one

156

note that can turn this nightmare around. Yes, yes, I can hear that the sopranos have picked it up along with the tenors and now the altos. This was accomplished in such a professional way that even the members of the orchestra were not aware of what happened. Now all the chorus is singing *a cappella* and the sound is just beautiful. Suddenly I see the most surprised look on Unal's face. In short, he forgot to turn the page for his solo note. By this time, it's just tough titty for old Unal as his starring role has just vaporised into thin air. However, it just goes to prove once again that no one person is indispensable in any given situation.

Most of the concert has been completed and we are coming to *Worthy Is The Lamb That Was Slain* followed by the *Amen*. With my right hand on the up beat I hit the music before me and pray that I haven't gone too far just in case I should have to refer to it. Not likely, but then again, you never know. You see, with my right hand devoted to the orchestra and my left hand devoted to the chorus one doesn't have a free hand to turn the musical score. People can laugh and make comments, but when you haven't directed a Symphony Orchestra before and then throw an 85 voice Choral Group in on top of it, you are asking for trouble and praying for a miracle to be performed. Scared, scared you ask? hell no, I've been terrified from the minute I walked on stage after being patched up.

Now we are into the *Amen* Chorus and the orchestra has taken off in one direction with the sopranos altos, tenors and basses all taking off in their own direction. Trying to keep the orchestra together and keep track of the four moving vocal parts is no place for a person with a one track mind. Now we are entering the final critical manoeuvering part of this selection. I now have the orchestra cornered along with the sopranos and tenors, but the altos and basses are still running free up and down the scale. Ah, now I gotcha as I grab onto the altos and basses. I now have the four vocal parts secured in my left hand and the orchestra secured in my right hand as we enter the final *Amen* . . . *A* . . . *A* . . . *Amen*. With the final *Amen*, the first performance is now concluded and has become history. With that, I looked up towards the ceiling and uttered a 'Thank You God' for that which has just come to pass. Tears of jubilation spring forth from my eyes as the applause is so deafening and I suddenly realise that I don't have to apologise to anyone for our performance which has just concluded. What a spine tingling feeling it is which bolts through my body, knowing against all odds and some people, we had pulled it off. Wild applause still rings forth as I slowly turn to the audience to accept their adulation. I then turn to have my orchestra and vocalists stand to accept them as well. I then leave the stage only to have to return again. I started to leave the stage once again but had no return when two ushers came forth bringing two very large baskets of flowers. They were red and white carnations. One was from the President and the other was from the Prime Minister. While acknowledging them, two more baskets of flowers arrived. What a night to remember in more ways than one. My mind flashed back to the beginning of this concert when I was placed in handcuffs and thought to be a terrible terrorist. Look at me now. Here I stand surrounded by beautiful red and white carnations, the national colours of Turkey. It could really blow one's mind as to how events could change so quickly especially when you find yourself in the middle of it.

Two lovely looking usherettes lead us to the front of the concert hall where a white marble stairway is located. As you start your descent you find it is a gradual sloping curving stairway to the right which leads to an elegant reception room located under the concert hall. The stairs are covered with a regal royal blue hand made Isparta carpet ending at the bottom of the stairs. The rest of this huge reception area is covered with various coloured Isparta rugs. From where I stand, the room seems to be about 75 feet long and approximately 40 feet wide. Running from both sides of the walls and across the back of the room are heavy velvet gold-coloured drapes. Twelve small, but beautiful crystal chandeliers were hanging from the ceiling. Later, the most intriguing revelation was revealed. Behind the heavy gold draperies were located 25 soundproof practice music rooms. Pretty smart these Turks.

As we look in the direction of the Presidential party, we can see the bulk of the foreign diplomatic corps, ladies, that is, making a big splash and trying to outdo each other for the attention of the President and his entourage. You know what? They all remind me of a swarm of bees buzzing around a large honey pot of sweet nectar. My God, what a buzzing sound they can conjure up. Right in the middle and in the thick of things is Mrs Blankenship who conceives herself as the Queen Bee of the Ankara Socialite World. While this is going on, I can see many of my friends on the other side of the room watching the proceedings and getting quite a bang out of the buzzing woman. At this point, Mrs Blankenship turns and sees Metin and I standing and watching the goings on. Like in a movie script, she turns and flitty floops over to where we are standing and proceeds to put on the second show of the evening. 'Oh Carl dear,' she exclaims in a loud voice, while placing her arm around my shoulder, 'your concert was just marvellously divine. Oh darling,' she continued, with a girlish giggle, 'I just have to mention how cute your bum was swaying back and forth with the beat of every note. It was', she continued again, 'just heavenly and out of this world.' You can sure tell her musical knowledge is less than zilch.

As I look up and turn my head to the right, I can see Hanna heading this way. At that split second I'm thinking, Mrs Blankenship, you had better get your arm off from across my shoulder or you'll be heading out of this world when Hanna is finished with you.

'*Mösyöciğim*, my Madam wants you to speak over there. Excuse me please lady,' as she takes Mrs Blankenship's arm off my shoulder. 'I take my *Mösyöciğim* away now.' With one strong jerk I'm off in the other direction, with Hanna looking back at Mrs Blankenship. Having just had the proverbial rug pulled from under her, she flitty flops back to her buzzing group and pretends that nothing has happened. However, everyone in range of Hanna's voice knows that Mrs Blankenship has been rebuffed pure and sweet. Pulling me by the arm, she was telling everyone that comes our way that this is her *Misurecigim*. She was as proud as a peacock and wanted everyone to know it.

'Hanna,' I said, 'did you bring Poppie with you this evening?' She looked at me and answered. 'No *Mösyöciğim*, I left that old man at home so he could play with his dirty pictures.'

'Hanna, shame on you for saying that.'

'No *Mösyöciğim*,' she continued, 'we old people no shame have.'

I just wondered how the newspapers will report this evening's events with all the Ankara social butterflies flapping around in all directions. It's almost like opening night's review by critics with their stinging remarks. In all fairness, I should point out that under normal circumstances, Hanna is a very gentle person. By the same token, she is very protective of her Madam and her *Mösyöciğim* and treats us like her own children. Further, you know just how protective a mother can be if she feels her children are being placed in any danger, real or imaginary. That's our Hanna, a living angel in our eyes.

'*Mösyöciğim*, why you all wet? Look Madam, my *Mösyöciğim* all wet head to foos (foot).'

'Hanna,' said Joyce Backhouse, 'your *Mösyöciğim* has been working very hard tonight on stage.'

'I no see him work hard. He only wave his arms at all those people in front of him.'

'Joyce,' I chimed in, 'please don't try to explain, as we could be here all night. She doesn't understand all the various pressures I was under or what I've been through. Perhaps, it's better that way as she won't worry.'

'You're probably right.'

It looks like the Presidential entourage is getting ready to depart and the Security Police are beginning to take up new positions. As the entourage starts to leave to get away from the buzzing and yakking women, the Naval aide said something to the President's party and he stopped and turned around. The aide motioned for me to come forward. Pointing my finger at myself, he nodded yes. Slowly I approached the President's group like a nervous prostitute being propositioned for the very first time. As I go forward, President Gürsel extends his hand and says as our hands meet. 'Congratulations for an excellent concert.'

'It is most kind of you to say that Mr President,' I think I said. Flash bulbs were popping all around us and the Security Police were none too happy having the press so close to us. With that, the President turned and ascended the grand stairway and departed the concert hall. Quick to follow up the stairway was the ladies' social group who found little or no interest in us who were the stars of the evening. Good luck to them. Joyce Backhouse, Hanna, the Count and Contessa De Cario, and a number of my military friends came over to where I was standing and we had a talking good time. I said, 'You know, there were a lot of firsts made here tonight when you stop and think about it. The Presidential Symphony Orchestra was never conducted by an American before, let alone an American Sergeant, the orchestra had never been combined with a choral group before, the choral group had never performed with an orchestra before, the first time such a programme was given in Turkey, the first time the Conductor was handcuffed prior to a concert, the first time I had ever conducted a Symphony Orchestra, the first time the Symphony Orchestra had ever been conducted without a baton and the first time I had ever met a real live President. That's a lot of firsts in anyone's language. Speaking of firsts, I don't want to be the first party pooper, but putting it mildly and bluntly, I'm just plain beat to hell. Okay, I'll see all of you tomorrow and thanks for all your help and understanding.

'Chaplain, the next to last time I was at your car here, it was damn near a catastrophe for all concerned. There was no way of my knowing that after 7.30 pm this area was closed and off limits to everyone. Not a word was put out concerning this area by either the police or by the Concert Hall Manager. However, it sure didn't take me long to find out that I was not permitted in that area. Frankly, they scared the piss right out of me, I kid you not.'

Having said good night to Chaplain Wilson, I start climbing these three flights of stairs which seems to be a bigger problem than usual. As I open the door, the landlord opens his door just across the hall and tells me that he and his wife enjoyed the concert very much. I thank him and close my door. I'm sure he now feels that he has a celebrity residing in his apartment building. Watch, he'll raise the rent tomorrow. As I remove my coat, I have a quick niff under my arm pits and pray that my deodorant didn't fail me. Nope, all seems okay with no foul odours coming forth. As usual, no damn water for a relaxing shower. I'll just have to settle for my birdie bath and then slide into the arms of Morpheus

My God, who in the hell is ringing my door bell at this time of the morning? I'm coming, I'm coming. As I open the door, a man in a black chauffeur's uniform is standing there pushing my door bell. 'Can I help you?' I sort of barked at him.

'Is this the Crocker residence?' with a voice that was trying to sound rather British upper class.

'With all things being equal,' I said, 'this sure in hell isn't Buckingham Palace. Yes, this is the Crocker residence.'

'This is an invitation to the Blankenship's Residence in six days time. It's RSVP. You do know what RSVP means or stands for do you not?'

'Far better than the person that has delivered the invitation, Sir,' I said with a smirk on my face. With that, I rather slammed the door in his face. Just what time is it? My God, it's now 1.30 pm in the afternoon and all this time I thought it was morning. Maybe I was a bit too sharp with the chauffeur, but that which is done, is done, so to hell with it. Now to get something to eat and start thinking about getting myself ready for tonight's concert. Oh yes, I must not forget the pink ribbon and the red ribbon for tonight.

'You're right on time Chaplain.'

'Yes Carl, I wouldn't dare be late being the task master as you are.'

'Ah, come off it Chaplain, I'm not a task master.'

'Well, if you are not you are in a darn good replica. What I'm really trying to say is this. Firstly, if you had been a little on the weak side we wouldn't have had the desire to do it. Secondly, if you had not been demanding at every turn we would have been lost.'

'I understand what you are trying to say Chaplain, but I can truthfully say, no one will ever know just how much this project has taken out of me.

'By the way Carl, just be sure you don't leave your coat in the car.'

'You just had to say that didn't you?'

When we get inside the Concert Hall the Chaplain goes his way and I go mine. I find Metin's little box in which he keeps the baton. Carefully opening the box I take out the baton and wrap it in pink ribbon. I'm sure after he sees my baton wrapped in pink ribbon he will never leave it again in the men's toilet. Next I find my Bass player's music and place a red ribbon across the page so he won't forget to turn the page.

The Symphony Orchestra and the Choral Group are now all on stage just waiting for me to make my entrance. I now see Metin open the box containing the carefully wrapped baton. With his expression on this face, he really doesn't know what to do with it. I'm standing in the wing laughing my head off. Metin struggles with the pink ribbon trying to get it off so he can place my baton on my music stand. He finally gets the sticky tape and the ribbon off and he is looking all around to see who had put it there. Of course, he is not looking in my direction or he would have found his answer. Turning my head, I look at the bass player and say to myself, brother do you also have a surprise coming. With all of the fooling out of the way, we start the concert. Of course, the audience was none the wiser as to what was taking place on stage.

We had gone nearly through the first half of the programme and the orchestra and chorus couldn't have performed or sounded better. I was so happy that all was going along so very well until one of the female soloists got up to do her solo. I don't know what happened, but she leaped up like a rocket being shot off from its launching pad and took two music stands and the music right along with her. It was her long flowing evening dress which got caught in the first music stand and swept the second music stand, music and all right with her. My mouth flew open in utter shock as the orchestra and chorus looked on like stunned mullet . . . Madam . . . soloist? It didn't faze her one iota.

She carried on like it was an every day occurrence and seemed oblivious to the fact that it was one huge bang like Jericho, when the walls came tumbling down. What did I do? Nothing. All that was to be done, was done.

Behind me I could hear a slight ripple from the audience, but it was short lived. At this point, more perspiration eased through my pores and into my suit. Oh God, at this rate I'll be water logged or drown in my own perspiration before we reach the Intermission. What in the hell makes you even think that you'll even reach the Intermission I contemplate to myself? Oh shut up and keep swinging your arms said the other little voice in my head. Now we start the *Hallelujah Chorus* and I hear many of the people starting to stand up. I like to think of it as the Seventh Inning Stretch to an American baseball game, as they have been sitting all this time on their backsides with some I'm sure having gone to sleep. Again, by them standing at this time, just before the Intermission, will give them a head start to the refreshment stand. We now reach the last four notes *Hall – le – lu – jah*! I now step down from my little hallowed box and leave the stage quick smart. Like Garbo, in the thirties, I want to be alone.

The soprano has now finished her little diatonic diddy and has been seated. As I look towards my bass player, you know, the one that damn near gave me a coronary attack last night, I see him frantically wrestling with his music. As I look closer, I can see some red ribbon attached to his music sheet. I smile and say to myself, I wonder how that red ribbon got attached to your music ha, ha. I wait just a second or two before I point to him for the one note I must hear to start the next chorus which is *a cappella* for the first twelve measures. Needless to say, he was right on cue but was still mystified as to how the red ribbon got mixed up in his music. Little does he know. Really, I guess the devil made me do it.

With the final blaze of glory from the orchestra and the chorus and at double *fortissimo*, I might add, now brings this concert to its brilliant conclusion. The tremendous applause given to us both nights of the concert tells a very complete picture of that which was presented. What the audience didn't hear or see didn't really detract from that which was presented. Case in point. When a passage of music didn't sound just right to me while being performed, it would invoke a special reaction from me. That is, if it was the chorus, my left hand on the up beat would cross under my nose and I would make a face at the chorus. That gesture meant that the passage stank. The same held true for the orchestra as well but only with the right hand. The message was conveyed. In short, they were quickly on their musical toes and the fault corrected spontaneously. On the plus side, this usually brought forth smiles from both the orchestra and chorus and projected a very happy illusionist image to the audience. It was very easy to understand why the audience thought we had such a very happy smiling organisation. If they only knew what was really going on in front of them. However, the tremendous applause which we are now receiving tells it all. The one thought that was going through my head again was, Thank you Lord, with your help we pulled it off. Amen.

After the concert, the entire group gathered downstairs in the reception room for the customary slapping of each other on the back and relating just how good we were under the circumstances etc. Now, we must prepare ourselves to re-enter the world of real life once more. Oh what stories these will make for my grandchildren. With a closing speech to my musical group, the concert has now become a part of recorded history.

As I open the door to the apartment, I've decided to have a good stiff bourbon and coke and just relax and reflect on these past few hellish months. Tomorrow being a regular work day, I'm wondering what general comments I'll be confronted with at work. Not to worry old boy, you know within yourself you did your very best and it turned out damn good. I'll just enjoy my drink and let nature take its course as tomorrow is unyet born and it doesn't belong to me.

My little bed feels so good tonight as the stress and pressure can nowhere be found. What a night it's going to be as I slowly slip off into the land of dreams.

As the house lights dim, a shining figure makes its way onto centre stage. The shining glittering of a gold costume steps upon the podium. As the baton is picked up there seems to be a glittering light on the end of the baton. When the spotlight is brought up it reveals none other than 'Bunny-Hop-A-Long-Blaire.' You know, he is the man that told me I had to direct this concert. What in the hell is he trying to do? There is no orchestra there or anyone else as a matter of fact on stage. There is music being played and the chorus is singing and it's the pro-gramme we have just completed. I just don't understand what's going on. He now turns and makes a low sweeping bow to an empty concert hall and the applause is thunderous. I just can't comprehend what's taking place. If I didn't know better, I would think that he is jealous of the successful concert and now he is trying to upstage all our efforts. I knew that he wanted praise, but I didn't think that he would go this far. He looks at me and snarls his upper lip and utters *Et tu Brute.*

Suddenly, the music changes and the orchestra that is not there is now playing David Rose's *The Stripper.* Taking on a new completion, Bunny Baby has now tossed his baton to the non existence audience and has started to strip in rhythm with the music. There goes his sparkling jacket with all the shining sequins flying in all directions as they detach themselves from his jacket. With his jacket seemingly suspended in mid air, the falling sequins seem to appear like swarms of fireflies darting to and fro with the beat of the music. He has now removed his sequined pants and is twirling them around his head like a real stripper. With each twirl, the centrifugal force releases more and more shining sequins than the one before. Standing on centre stage in his Barber Pole "long johns" he looks at me and lets out a huge belly laugh. 'See you stupid fool,' he shouts at me, 'that's how you direct a Symphony Orchestra plus giving your audience something to stimulate their sexual hallucinations.'

'You're sick, you're sick,' I shout back at him.

'You ain't seen nothing yet, as he starts to remove his Barber Pole Long Johns'. At this precise moment, Mrs Blankenship and her 'social butterflies', all eight of them come sliding down from wires leading from the giant organ pipes at the rear of the stage. Dressed in flimsy see-through Butterfly costumes, they leave little or nothing for the imagination to play with. They danced around the stage and around Bunny like little fairies in a story book. Oh my God, what can I do, as this is beginning to turn into a sex orgy as Mrs Blankenship has somehow wrapped her body around Bunny's body. Shouts of approval roar from the non-existent audience. 'More, more,' they shout as Bunny starts to lower the bottom part of his Barber Pole long johns exposing a pinkish ass which he is palpitating back and forth minus any G-String or any other attachments. With his back towards the audience he turns his head slowly around and smiles at them just waiting for them to beg him to turn around and show them the wonders of his precious hanging gardens. I'm so damn embarrassed about the entire situation I just turn my head in disgust. Suddenly, I hear a loud bloodcurdling and terrifying scream coming from Bunny. Quickly turning my head, I see Hanna standing there in her horse riding outfit behind

Bunny and playing a joyful tune on his bare ass with a riding crop. 'Hanna, Hanna,' I shout, 'what are you doing?'

'*Mösyöciğim*,' she calls back, 'this is dirty old man almost like Poppie. Poppie only looks at dirty pictures, but this man is a dirty dirty old man,' as she gives him another swat across the buttocks. He tries to run away from her, but she belts him again across his bare buttocks.

'Hanna, where did you come by the riding outfit and riding crop?'

'Oh *Mösyöciğim*,' she smiles, 'this belongs to my friend, you know, when he used to go horse riding and he no mind if I put to good use.' She turns to give Bunny another crack across the buttocks but everything has vanished leaving only the darkened stage and a ringing bell. After searching and searching for the ringing bell, I finally knock the alarm clock off the night stand by the bed and onto the floor. There was a lot of pushing and shoving but I hurry back into my body to start another day. Lying here in bed all nice and cosy and relaxed, my mind ponders over the past three and a half months knowing that it has finally come to a happy ending. Of course there is till one more hurdle to jump and that is Mrs Blankenship's party on Saturday night. After that, the concert will be well and truly finished and buried. Frankly, I really don't know why I told them that I would be attending. The cream of the Ankara social society I'm sure will be on hand to be seen and heard. They will be wearing their diamonds, real or otherwise, and all carrying their gold plated lorgnettes and flashing them about as if they too were the real McCoy. I'm sure they will all check with their fabulous dress-makers to insure that each will be wearing an original new creation. It's a safe bet to say that even New York or Hollywood hasn't seen anything like these Social Butterflies. As I say, seeing is believing. Oh yes, should you desire to find out the latest gossip, who is sleeping with whom, just ask the off beat question and they will be most happy to oblige even to the real juicy intimacy of the relationship. I'm sure that they must have some valued place in our society, or else the good Lord wouldn't have created so many of them.

Do my ears deceive me, or is that the water I hear running next door? It's the water alright. Now for a quick and refreshing shower before work. Would you look at that? I just can't believe what the scales say. If it's true, Weight Watchers would be most happy with my results. I've lost 16 pounds in three and a half months. I guess I could write a book on how to lose weight without really trying. Better yet, know to build up your bank account . . . just stop eating. The shower sure felt good, so I had better get dressed, have a wee bit of something to eat, and then be off to work.

As I make my way up to Atatürk Boulevarde I can see the Russians and the street sweepers, Turkish Secret Police, that is, are at it in full swing as usual. If they keep sweeping and cleaning the very same spot all the time, they are soon going to wear the pavement out long before the traffic does. That's the Cold War for you.

'Good morning Mrs Dençir, you are in a little early this morning.'

'Good morning Carcigim. Yes, I'm a little early this morning as I want to finish my letter to my son so I can mail it at lunch time today. He's the son that's in New York City working for IBM.'

'Oh yes, I remember you mentioning it. He wants to know when I was planning my vacation so I could come and visit and see their new baby. It is very difficult with my daughter in the University here to manage the visit there.'

'We'll see.'

'Carcigim, how is Hanna and her family?'

'I assume the family is all well, as she hasn't indicated that any of them are sick or anything like that. However, as for Hanna, she is still Hanna and as unpredictable as usual. I'm sure that I didn't tell you what happened this week when the Team Chiefs came into JUSMMAT for their yearly meeting. If you recall you have met Colonel Barlow, Lt Col Bright, Lt Col Rush, Major Smith and Lt Col Higgins when they came in from Erzurum. These meetings are such a drag I thought that it would be nice to have them over for lunch and let them relax and enjoy a good home cooked meal. They all agreed and seemed very happy about it. I informed Hanna that there would be five people plus myself for lunch on Wednesday. Mrs "D" she was most happy as she really likes to get into the kitchen and cook up a storm. She got all excited and started jumping around like a Mexican Jumping Bean. I left her 400 Lira and told her to fix what she liked but not to work too hard.

'Oh no *Mösyöciğim*,' she said to me, 'I no hard work.'

'You could see that she was like a volcano ready to erupt with enthusiasm at any second.'

On Wednesday afternoon we all arrived together at the apartment and Hanna was at the door to greet us with a big smile and a hug for me. She had the table set with the good china and silverware and even had the silver plated champagne goblets on instead of the smaller silver plated wine goblets. What the hell, she had done a fantastic job and the table looked just great. When everyone had entered, and had taken their jackets off, without giving me a chance to introduce her, she announced that she was Hanna. They all responded with we are pleased to meet you Hanna. She responded by putting her head to one side and let forth with a little giggle like a young school girl would. She was now in her element and nothing was going to rain on her parade. I looked at her and saw that she even had made a new apron which matched her shining eyes and glowing personality. Needless to state, this was her shining hour, and the Gods were on hand to see that it belonged to her. Prior to lunch, some had a cold beer, wine or water. You could just feel the relaxed atmosphere and even Hanna was humming in the kitchen while working. While she was at it, she remembered to venture forth to remind everyone present, that today they should all big eat as she fixed plenty of food. looking at everyone she remarked again 'everyone big eat today.' A few minutes had elapsed when she announced that we should all take our places at the table. 'Colonel Barlow you sit at head of table, and my *Mösyöciğim* will sit here, close to the kitchen door.' I guess I should have had mentioned to Hanna that Lt Col Higgins was on a diet and was losing weight, but the thought didn't cross my mind. The smell of that food coming from the kitchen was just out of this world. Shortly, Hanna announced again that we should all get to the table as she was about to bring in the food. Seated at the head of the table was Colonel Barlow, to his left was Lt Col Higgins, to his left was Major Smith, to his left was me, and to my left was Lt Col Bright and then came Lt Col Rush. First to come in was the golden brown *Weiner Schnitzel* which she served to Lt Col Higgins. Lt Col Higgins took a rather small helping of the *Weiner Schnitzel* to which Hanna took note. Next came the fluffy white mashed potatoes with melted butter on top garnished with paprika which livened it up to make it more pleasing to the eye and palate. This was followed by tender peas and carrots in soft creamy white sauce. Now came the steamy home made hot biscuits wrapped in a linen cloth to keep them really hot. I can truly say that there wasn't much conversation bouncing around the table, but only the sound of food being consumed. Hanna was standing right behind me and savouring every munching sound. Quick as a flash Hanna said, '*Mösyöciğim*, Sarap, you know *Mösyöciğim*, Sarap.' Major Smith leaned over and wanted to know why Hanna was telling me to 'shut-up'. When Hanna said Sarap to me the third time, the rest of the group looked up and was wondering what had gone wrong. Had they missed something while they were busy eating? I started to laugh and shake my head. 'Gentlemen,' I said, 'nothing has gone wrong, except that I have forgotten to pour the excellent Kavaklidere Wine. Hanna was only saying Sarap gentlemen, which sounds in English like shut-up.' A big laugh went around the table. Once the wine was poured I sat down but Hanna had the *Weiner Schnitzel* and was standing at Lt Col Higgins' side. 'Please Colonel,' she insisted.

'Oh Hanna, I had so much I'm really full.'

Looking at him she handed the platter of *Weiner Schnitzel* to Lt Col Rush. By this time, Lt Col Higgins had pushed himself a wee bit back from the table and patted his stomach area to show Hanna that he was full. Hanna didn't buy it. She reached down with her right hand pulling the belt and trousers away from the stomach area and with her left hand placed it between the belt and the stomach. 'See,' she said, 'you no big eat.' All of a sudden she screamed and Lt Col Higgins let out a huge laugh. It seems that Hanna had made contact with his *Weiner* and I've just had the *Schnitzel*. Pandemonium broke forth and I slid partly under the table while still sitting in my chair. This was nothing as to the encore which was about to follow. Laughing at the top of her voice, she looked at me and screamed, 'Oh *Mösyöciğim*, I very much like my hand to put in men's pants.' That's really not what she meant, but that is the way it came out. As a closing note on the luncheon episode, Mrs "D" they all sent Hanna flowers and chocolates before heading back to Erzurum. Oh yes, Lt Col Higgins wrote in his note to Hanna, that he would like to do it all over again, but he didn't state what.

Being Friday, I've been invited to go to Armando's mother's home for dinner. Elaine told me when I saw her on my way home from work yesterday. If you thought that the United Nations had problems with various languages, look at this line-up just for an informal dinner party. First off, Armando's mother is Italian but is currently married to a Greek living in Turkey. She speaks Italian, Greek and Turkish. Her husband speaks a little Turkish and of course Greek. Armando, by the way is a real Italian Count, Count De Corio and he speaks Italian, Turkish and English, which he murders, plus Mexican. He works in the Mexican Consul General's Office. Armando's sister who was married to a German but now is divorced and presently married to an Argentinian, speaks Italian, German, Turkish and Spanish. Her young daughter by her first marriage speaks French, Italian, German, Spanish and Turkish. As for Elaine, the Contessa De Cario, she speaks English and Turkish. As for me, I speak a little German, English, Turkish and Japanese. With just a little twist of your imagination you can quickly conjure up many funny situations taking place at the dinner table. Bouncing from one language to the next all evening surely didn't leave much time to enjoy an excellent meal. If you don't think it's trying and funny, try it sometime . . . please pass the aspirin. It was a lovely dinner, but frankly, I'm just happy that it is over with.

'Hanna, did they return my black suit from the cleaner?'

'Yes *Mösyöciğim*, I made sure that it was ready because I went and picked it up for you. I also had that pretty little white bow tie cleaned as well as it makes you look very pretty man.'

'Thank you Hanna, but I'll wear the other tie as the white tie makes me look like a waiter.'

'No *Mösyöciğim*, makes you look very pretty, so you wear pretty white tie.'

'Very well Hanna, but I'm sure I won't like it.' The things I put up with and do just to keep the peace.

'Okay *Mösyöciğim* , I home now go to see what Poppie has been up to. Everything for you is all ready.'

'Give my hello's and love to Poppie, will you Hanna?'

'Yes *Muirecigim*.'

Saturday afternoon has arrived and soon it will be time for me to start thinking about getting ready to attend Mrs Blankenship's party up in Çankaya it being one of the better areas of Ankara sits high on a hill overlooking the entire city with a sea of blinking lights. It's a very beautiful sight. The word Çankaya seems to have two meanings. *Çan* means (Bell) while *Kaya* means (Rock). If you take the *Çan*, I would say yes there are sure a lot of *Ding Dongs* in the area. Even the President's Palace is located in Çankaya. However, I do not mean to imply or even to infer that any of them are *Ding Dongs*. Words are funny when you take them out of their real context. It's been going on for thousands of years so I guess it will continue.

Mrs Blankenship's son is one of the 'big wigs' in the US AID programme here in Turkey. It would go without saying that they would have to live in one of the better sections of Ankara due to his status. It would sure be a lot better if I was just going to a party instead of being elevated to the guest of honour status by Mrs Blankenship. I'm sure that this is just one of her ways of showing the other Social Butterflies that she is still queen of the Social Set by having this type of party where she can show off and strut her stuff, whatever that may be. When I accepted this invitation I thought that it would be a fun thing and be sort of a swinging party with lots of laughs etc. As the time is drawing near to get myself ready I'm beginning to have second thoughts. The reason behind this is, that I have checked with several friends whom I believe should have been invited but their names just don't appear on the invitation list. Two are Chaplain Wilson and Mrs Joyce Backhouse. So the list goes on of people not invited. I'm beginning to wonder what kind of a social party this is going to turn into? I guess time will tell.

Hanna has laid out by black suit along with my little white clip-on bow tie. On a number of occasions I have told her that this clip-on bow tie makes me look like a waiter. However, she contends that when I wear it I look pretty. Well, if it pleases her I guess it is worth it. Anything to keep peace on the home front.

With a bit of time on my hands prior to getting dressed and leaving for the party, a nice relaxing drink may just be on the cards. Selecting a bourbon and coke seems to be just the ticket to relax oneself and mind. Putting on a record or two seems only to add to the relaxed feeling and it's just great.

Yak! I got so relaxed that I dropped off for a couple of winks which was such a good feeling. Even the record player managed to turn off, so I must have had a good snooze. I can only say I must have needed it. I'll give my shoes a quick brush or two and proceed slowly to get myself dressed for my big coming out party. Being the guest of honour I'm wondering if they will ask me to say a few chosen words? If not, they will probably drink a toast to me at least and let it go at that.

If I take a taxi, I should arrive in ample time prior to 8.30 pm with time to spare. I'm sure you have heard the old saying. 'The trouble with being punctual is that there is no one there to appreciate it.' Then again, you don't want to be late and you do desire to make a good impression. I must admit or confess that I have never met Stewart Blankenship and I wouldn't know him from Santa Claus or the Good Tooth Fairy. Besides all that, I'm looking forward to meeting him. Just one more sip from my bourbon and coke and I'll be off up to Atatürk Boulevarde to look for a taxi.

Taxi! . . . Taxi! Damn it, there goes three of them and they didn't even slow down or stop. Taxi . . . , yep . . . he stopped, but it seems like a rather old and beat up taxi and I have my doubts if it can make it up the steep hill to Çankaya where I have to go. 'Where are you going?' he asks in Turkish.

'I'm going to Çankaya near the Subay Klub (Officers' Club),' I answered in Turkish. 'Will your taxi make it up the hill?' I ask in Turkish.

His response, in Turkish, *'Inşallah,'* (If God wills). Frankly, that surely scares the hell of me as that isn't a real positive answer. Cautiously and with reservation I slowly get into the taxi with the taxi driver smiling all the time. I have a feeling that he is thinking more about the fare and not about whether his taxi can make it up the steep hill to Çankaya. As we start up Atatürk Boulevarde towards Çankaya and on to Dr Resat Vali Caddesi, the old car sputters, jerks and groans but grinds slowly up the hill. When I was beginning to think that we are going to make it, nearly half way up the hill, the old car gave a couple of jerks and sputters and stopped right in the middle of the road. Complete fear took over as we started to roll backward down the hill. Still smiling, the taxi driver in all his wisdom finally found and pulled on the hand brake and eased the car back into the curb. Holy cow, I nearly had a loose bowel movement right there in the back seat of the taxi. When we were secured against the curb, the driver got out and lifted the hood and with a hand wrench gave something a bank or two and then closed the hood.

'Tamam,' he said in Turkish, which means it's finished. This left me a very wide selection to choose from. One, it's finished, meaning the motor. Two, bang bang made everything right again. Three, the car has died on the spot. Four, he, the taxi driver, is finished. Five, if I stay in the car I'm finished . . . or six, we are now going to proceed. What a group of options to choose from. I started to get out of the taxi, but Smiley, as I have now named him, said in Turkish that we were ready to go up the hill once more. I told him that I would get out of the taxi and let him get a head start but he wouldn't buy into that. His theory as best as I could make out was once the car got going he might not be able to stop, pick me up and start going again. Come to think about it, I wasn't quite sure if I gave a damn about it or not. I'm still in one piece, no broken bones, but still scared. I've come this far, so what the hell. I got back into the car and closed the door. Smiley was still smiling. He started the engine, stepped on the gas, released the hand brake, let out the clutch and we leaped forward like a frog leaping off a lily pad. With a loud bang we started up the hill once more leaving behind

a big cloud of black smoke like a steam train pulling out of the local train station and in one helluva hurry. I don't know what he tapped under the hood, but whatever it was catapulted us straight past two other vehicles like they were tied to a fence post. As we neared the top of Dr Resat Vali Caddesi, Smiley, the taxi driver, didn't seem to slow down but whizzed right past two more vehicles. When we arrived at the Officers' Club, he reached down and pulled on the hand brake. Taking it out of gear, the engine was still racing on. It seems he had pushed so hard on the hill on the accelerator that it jammed into the floor board along with part of his shoe with the foot still in it. He now reached over and turned off the roaring engine. By this time a number of people in the club were staring from the bay windows and pointing at us. I had the sudden feeling that they thought the taxi was going to blow up and take part of the club with it. I was white around the gills as I stepped forth from the taxi and didn't quite seem to have my sea legs so to speak under me. At first glance, one could rightfully think that I was under the influence, but I can assure you that I wasn't. Anything would have been possible after that ride. Composing myself, I reached into my wallet and gave the taxi driver thirty lira for a ten lira ride. It was hoped that he would take the extra money and get started on some of the repairs that his taxi most urgently required. He was thanking me over and over again, until I turned and walked away. When I reached the top of Dr Resat Vali Caddesi, I walked until I reached the Blankenship home. Looking at my watch, I was about two minutes ahead of schedule for my 8.30 pm appointment. Wanting to make a good impression, I waited until it was 8.30 pm sharp and then rang the door bell. From the time I rang, it seemed like five minutes had elapsed before anyone came to the front door. As they were coming, I made sure that my little white clip on bow tie was straight and I was all tucked in properly. As I entered, the maid said to me, 'Well, it's about time that you got here, you're late you know.' I just smiled as I entered the foyer. I looked around and there was a beautiful winding stairway which lead up to the second floor.

'Just don't stand there,' she commanded, 'all the food and things have to be put out and the bar has to be set up. You'll find the glasses in the kitchen along with the ice in the ice making machine.'

At this time I was of two minds. This situation was so hilarious that I thought I would go along with it, while my other thought was that it's a send up. In either case, I would be laughed at.

'When you want the ice from the machine, there is a bucket here which is used for that.' Suddenly I start laughing and the maid, Fatma, that's her name, wanted to know what was so funny. I looked at her and said, 'Nothing.' What I really was laughing at was that which I had told Hanna about my little white clip-on bow tie making me look like a waiter. Now here I am acting out the part. While I was setting up the bar, a man in his forties came downstairs, over to the bar and requested a scotch on the rocks and be sure it was Johnny Walker Black Label he stated. I smiled at the man but he only glared like I had just insulted him. Piss on you, you old son-of-a-bitch was my passing thought as he made his way back up the stairs with his Johnny Walker Black Label in his hand.

'Fatma, do you have any nuts at the bar or do they only come with the male guests?'

No sense of humour as she gave me a rather cold look. Back and forth we both went, working like Trojans trying to stem the onslaught of arriving guests, keep them happy and our heads above water. Not an easy task when the Social Butterflies all swarm together in one spot. Such buzzing you have never heard.

'I'll have a Manhattan with two cherries please,' requested Sylvia Waters.'

'Make mine the same,' chimed in three more of the butterflies, Janice, Helen and Maggie.

'Just look at that cute bartender' Judy remarked to Lois Green.

'I don't recall seeing him on the Social Circuit before.'

'Maybe we had better get Maree Blankenship to introduce him to us already yet.'

'Look at his smile and his blue eyes and that little white bow tie which just sets him off. Cute he is already yet.' Checking the time quickly, I see that it is nearing 9.45 pm and the old 'Queen' of the Social Set is just now making her grand entrance. As she stands at the head of the staircase, she gazes down on her loyal social subjects, as they all turn and gaze up at her, each with thoughts of their own. She is dressed in a beautiful floor length emerald green gown, low cut cleavage, trying to expose that which is now long past exposing, but still hoping for the best. Around her shoulders, crossing down under her arms she is wearing a highly starched green very thin mesh which sets off her dyed red hair. While standing at the top of the staircase, she awaits her son Stewart to escort her down the stairs like the Queen of

174

Sheba. Having seen this kind of crap in the movies which Hollywood has dished out over the years, I never in my wildest dreams ever thought that in my young life I would live to see this acted out in real life. As she descended the staircase with her son, on his arm, she heads toward the bar after stopping several times to acknowledge guests who were chatting with her. 'Carl darling, what for ever on earth are you doing behind the bar?'

'Good question Mrs Blankenship.' Fatma enters bringing more appetisers and blows a fuse because I'm speaking with Mrs Blankenship.

'Go to the kitchen and get some more clean glasses,' is the order from Fatma.

'Fatma, if you want more clean glasses, may I suggest you go to the kitchen and get them yourself.' Having questioned her authority to order me about, Fatma becomes completely undone and dashes back to the kitchen fuming. Turning back once again to Mrs Blankenship I smile and continue my conversation with her.

'It seems that the bartender you hired just didn't show up and Fatma thought that I was the person you hired. Between us we have set up everything for your party and have been attending to your guests. Needless to say, it's been an education and a half.'

'Oh Stewart, this is Carl, you know, who was the director of the Symphony Orchestra and Chorus,' and with a little giggle, said, 'is our guest of honour this evening.'

'I'm very pleased to meet you.'

'By the way, will you forgive my rudeness earlier this evening, I'm very sorry.'

'Well, Mr Blankenship you know yourself better than I do. Mrs Blankenship, you will forgive me, I'm sure, but I'm now leaving.'

'Carl darling, the party is just beginning.'

'Thank you Mrs Blankenship, but the party has just ended for me. Goodnight.'